Elsie

The Percheron
Horse in America

The Percheron Horse in America

Joseph Mischka

Heart Prairie Press

Published by:
Heart Prairie Press
P.O. Box 332
Whitewater, WI 53190

Publisher's Cataloging in Publication

Mischka, Joseph, 1963-
    The Percheron horse in America / Joseph Mischka. --

    p. cm.
    Includes index and bibliographical references.
    ISBN 0-9622663-5-3

    1. Percheron horse — United States — History. I. Title.

SF293.P4   636.15
                                         QBI91-319

Printed in the United States of America

Dedication

This book is dedicated to my wife, Susan.

Acknowledgments

In researching this history, I drew from several sources which I am pleased to acknowledge and thank.

Alex Christian, Secretary of the Percheron Horse Association of America, furnished a great many reports, publications and other materials from the Association office. Elaine Christian, also of the Association office, was a great help in locating research items.

Many of the details regarding the history of Oaklawn Farm were given me through the gracious assistance of Jane Dunham, granddaughter of Mark Dunham, who founded Oaklawn Farm in Wayne, Ill.

Contents

Preface ix

Looking Back at the Percheron 1

A Breed Born of Battle 25

Arriving in the New World 33

A History of the Percheron Association of America 41
    Birth Pains (1876-1902) 42
    Establishing Credibility (1905-1910) 48
    The Glory Years (1911-1931) 70
    The End of an Era (1931-1948) 82
    Hard Times (1949-1981) 100
    The Modern Association (1981-1991) 108

Prominent Figures 119
    Oaklawn Farm and the Brilliants 120
    White, Butler and Laet 136
    Lynnwood Farm and Don Again 146

Appendix 153
    Timeline of Percheron History 154
    Association Officers 156
    Percheron Registration Totals by Year 158
    Premier Sires 159
    Grand Champion Stallions at National Shows 160

Index 161

Preface

The work horse contributed significantly to the development of America during the nineteenth and early twentieth centuries. During this period, the population of American settlers — and the territories they occupied — continued to increase. Heavy horses also grew both in terms of their numbers and their size, providing the strength to power the fast and furious expansion of the U.S.

That the horse helped build America is well understood by most. What is less known, however, is that the Percheron was by far the most prominent breed of heavy horses used during this period.

The first Percherons were established in America in the 1840s. By 1915 nearly 40,000 Percheron broodmares were registered in the U.S. **There soon were nearly three times more Percherons on America's farms, in her cities and on her roads, than all other draft horses combined.** The Percheron horse was the preferred breed of draft horse at the time heavy horses were so crucial for day-to-day living.

The story of the Percheron's rise to such prominence is worth telling. The last time it was told was when Alvin Sanders and Wayne Dinsmore published *A History of the Percheron Horse* in 1917. A lot has happened since then. This volume is an attempt to bring the story up to date.

Looking Back
at the Percheron

*The Horse that
Powered America*

The Horse That Powered America

During the first half of the twentieth century, when people spoke of draft horses — especially registered draft horses — they were probably speaking of Percherons. Up to World War II, Percherons outnumbered all other draft horse breeds combined by almost three to one.

American farmers preferred Percherons in their fields for their size, strength and speed. The Percheron was favored by city teamsters as well. In the city, firms which delivered coal, beer,

Photo Courtesy of Robert F. Hildebrand

Percherons were the preferred source of registered draft horse power in America during most of the nation's horse-powered days.

milk, ice and other household goods often used Percherons because the animal was alert, smart, attractive and quick.

An especially dramatic example of the Percheron's popularity can be found in the history of America's circuses. From the early 1870s to the late 1930s, the circuses of America were moved by horsepower — first from town to town, then later, from railroad yards to circus lots. By far, the breed of choice among the circus horsemen was the Percheron. In a letter written by Will Brock, who drove an eight-horse hitch for the Barnum & Bailey Greatest Show on Earth, he explained why the Percheron was so popular:

"The horses are grey because they are Percherons, for they are best adapted to the circus of all breeds. The baggage horse first of all must 'car' well, travel in the stockcar every night and not look as though he had no care or feed for a week when you unload him in the morning, with a good portion of the town out to look you over to judge by the looks of the horses what the show was likely to be. The Percheron comes out of the car in the morning looking as well

Circuses, which used massive numbers of draft horses to pull their wagons from town to town and later, from the railroad to the circus lot, preferred Percherons.

as when he went in. They are naturally solid, smoother turned and well filled and stand hard work under adverse conditions such as soft lots under scorching sun. . . They can stand more and they do not show the strenuous work they have been through when other teams of different breeds come out on the street looking like a hat rack."[1]

More information on how the Percheron horse served the great American circuses, can be found in Charles Philip Fox's book, *Circus Baggage Stock, A Tribute to the Percheron Horse.[2]*

The Percheron, it seemed, feared no competition. No other breed of draft horse showed any sign of encroaching on the Percheron's dominance. The reign of the Percheron was short-lived, however, as another form of motive power came along. The future for the Percheron horse, and the horsedrawn era in general, became bleaker with each mechanical innovation made in the tractor and truck industry, despite the many pleas, arguments and rationalizations made by staunch supporters of the Percheron industry to stay the course with horses.

American Percheron Industry Comes Into Its Own

In the late 1800s and very early 1900s, Percherons were usually imported to the United States from France rather than raised in the states. In other words, while the U.S. preferred Percherons, it was dependent upon France to furnish the horses.

During the first part of the twentieth century, however, the American Percheron industry came into its own. Early in World War I, American breeders of the day raised and exported record numbers of Percherons to Europe. American Percheron breeders imported fewer horses from the Perche District of France, and instead used more American-bred stock for breeding purposes.

The wartime demand for agriculture products such as oats, wheat and corn made the draft horse a vital part of the war effort at home. Breeders were encouraged to breed more and bigger horses to work on the farm. And while demand rose at home for draft power in the fields, horses were also needed to serve in the frontlines. Despite the fact that many motorized vehicles were developed for war, horses were still preferred for a variety of battlefield tasks, according to Society Secretary Wayne Dinsmore.

"Whatever may have been the ideas of army men prior to the war, it took but a very brief time to convince them that however

valuable motor trucks and tractors may be in transport work, horses alone could be relied upon to put men and artillery positions where needed."[3]

Indeed, great numbers of horses were called upon to furnish the necessary military power. U.S. officials of the day recorded that from Sept. 1, 1914, to Feb. 1, 1916, a total of 542,602 head of horses were exported from the U.S. to Europe for a total value of almost $115 million.[4]

French Horse Industry Suffers

While demand rose for horses, American Percheron breeders were forced to cease importing stock from France when the French imposed an embargo on the exportation of Percherons at the outbreak of the war. Importations of French horses fell off dramatically in 1915 when only 155 Percherons were imported to the U.S., compared to the 1,125 Percheron imports of the year before.[5]

Photo Courtesy of J.C. Allen and Son

Demand for agricultural goods during World War I, coupled with a shortage of labor, forced many farmers to use larger hitches on their farms.

At the time, French officials predicted that the embargo would remain active until at least six months after the end of the war. (The embargo was actually briefly lifted in April, 1916, to allow 59 Percherons to be imported to the U.S.)

Because most of the horses, fodder and horsemen in France were requisitioned for the war, the question of an embargo was moot, however, as the French could offer neither the numbers nor quality of Percheron horses American breeders had come to expect.

The French government purchased no stallions during the war, but many were gelded by their owners to be sold as work horses at premium prices.

In France, it was clearly simpler, and more profitable — at least in the short run — for horsemen to sell their stock quickly rather than keep them through the winter of 1915-1916 with short supplies of feed and fodder, said a French breeder in a letter published in the December 1915 Breeder's Gazette:

"We have cancelled nearly all our bargains with small breeders. We have reduced the number taken as much as possible, and we have acted wisely, as all the oats and barley have been taken for army supplies. It is even a question of taking bran at this time. I ask myself with anxiety how we are going to keep our animals alive up to the new harvest."

U.S. Percheron Industry Booms

While the situation in France spelled hard times for horse breeding there, American Percheron breeders were prepared to make up the ground lost by their French counterparts. At that time, Society records indicated that about 37,000 Percheron broodmares were registered in the U.S., and almost 10,000 colts were being produced annually. America was clearly a leader in the Percheron horse business for the first time.

But a formidable enemy of the work horse loomed on the horizon.

Tractors and Trucks

In the 1916 Percheron Review, Dinsmore discussed what must have been a prevalent and pressing concern to most draft horse farmers — whether the draft horse would be displaced by the developing tractor and truck industry.

Dinsmore argued that while "the pleasure car, vastly reduced in cost, and supplemented by rapid improvement in roads, has virtually eliminated the driving and coach horse," the tractor posed little threat to the draft horse's prominence in American farm fields.

"The use of tractors cannot be rated as profitable, even on larger farms, save where power work around the barns is relied upon to keep them busy a good share of the time, and their field work must be considered a secondary item, rather than the main point in their purchase. There is, however, only one cure for a man once thoroughly infected with the tractor fever, and that is the purchase of a tractor. Experience is a sure teacher."[6]

At the time, Dinsmore was right.

The horse was indeed slowly being edged off the city streets. The city of

Stallion trailers like these were used to haul breeding sires from farm to farm.

Chicago licensed all vehicles operating within its limits. In April, 1916, Chicago had licensed 49,682 horse-drawn vehicles and only 7,384 trucks. A year later, horse-drawn numbers had dropped to 46,470, a decline of 3,212; and trucks had risen to 11,530, a gain of 4,146.

In the field it was a different story. Horses were in demand on the homefront both before and after the U.S. abandoned its neutral stance and entered the war in 1917. The need for food supplies by American and other Allied troops — and the lack of available manpower at home — had farmers seeking larger teams and implements to work their fields.

Horses 1,600 pounds or larger which moved at a quick walk were the qualities these farmers wanted, and most found these qualities in Percherons. Dinsmore encouraged Percheron breeders to vigorously produce quality animals by playing to their patriotic as well as their pragmatic senses:

"Percheron breeders have now before them the greatest opportunity breeders of purebred horses have ever had. Prices realized by farmers for good Percherons are steadily advancing. More than

Photo Courtesy of Percheron Horse Association

When horses delivered the beer, Percherons were often the breed selected to do the job. Percherons were also used to deliver such things as ice, milk, coal, oil, furniture, and other household goods.

3,000 transfer certificates were issued by the Percheron Society of America during the four months ending March 1, 1917 — an increase of more than sixteen percent over the same period during the preceding year. Importations are practically nil, the demand for good Percherons is steadily increasing, and values are on a strictly utility basis. Personal profit, and service to our country alike, dictate one course — to breed every Percheron mare to the best available stallion, and so rear the foals and yearlings as to make them available for actual service when they are two years old."[7]

Dinsmore's sentiment was similarly expressed by then U.S. Secretary of Agriculture D.F. Houston:

"On account of the great scarcity of farm labor, greater use of horse power will be necessary to economic crop production. Because of this fact and the fact that the war demand will no doubt make large demands on our horse supply, every good mare should be bred in order to produce stock to replace those which

While this scene of Percheron mares and foals may still be found in parts of America today, it was much more common in the first half of the century.

will be used for war purposes. These mares should be bred to the best stallions available, keeping in mind that the market will be good for high-class horses, while the market for the inferior horse is very uncertain under the best conditions."[8]

The call for good horses continued in 1918 and Dinsmore turned up the volume on his plea for larger, heavier horses. The war had all but exhausted the available supply of large horses, and too few mares were being bred to fill the gap, Dinsmore wrote.

"In 1914, at the outbreak of the war, the United States had a vast surplus of horses ranging from 1,000 to 1,500 pounds. That surplus is now nearly exhausted. Horse buyers who formerly had no trouble buying two carloads per week, now come in with half a car, because they cannot buy more in a week's time. Farmers sold

Photo Courtesy of Percheron Horse Association

Draft horses were used for more than field work on the farm. They provided other power as well. Here, the team is pulling the hay pile into the barn by a series of pulleys.

themselves short last summer and fall because of the high price of feed. They are now searching for teams with which to do their spring work in 1918. As a result, prices have advanced appreciably in the last 30 days. Grade draft mares of good type, and sound, are fifty dollars per head higher than they were in December, and are increasing in value. Men who lack teams will pay so much for them this season that they will conclude that it is cheaper to raise work horses than to buy them."[9]

With the end of the war in 1918, American Percheron breeding resumed as feed became more available. Horse farms and available stock in the Perche District of France were more deeply hurt by the war, however, and would recover more slowly.

The question of the day had become less to do with whether horses would be displaced by tractors, but rather, how much displacement was likely to occur and how soon.

Photo Courtesy of Percheron Horse Association

A pair of well-matched Percherons pulling a manure spreader at a pretty good pace. The team is clean, upstanding and alert. Many farmers took special pride in the appearance of their farm teams.

"Horse Breeding Languishes"

In 1923, Illinois horseman E.T. Robbins stated that, largely due to the fear of the tractor, "horse breeding languishes."[9]

Robbins presented a variety of arguments — many of them philosophical, almost approaching sentimentality, but compelling, nevertheless — that favored the use of horses over tractors as farm power.

"Horses harmonize with farming. They are living things, as are the other livestock and the growing crops. The successful farmer has a natural solitude for the welfare of animals and plants. His interest centers in these living things which constitute the farm's source of income. The farmer whose interest centers in his machin-

Photo Courtesy of Philip Weber

Three Percherons pull the the last horsedrawn fire engine in Washington, D.C. during its last run before being retired in 1922.

ery should seriously consider changing his occupation. It is hard to make money when one takes more pride in his sources of expense than he does in his sources of income. The man who always hankers for another new machine should be running a factory and not a farm.

"Horse farming encourages steady work. The exceedingly long days and high speed in which the tractor may indulge at times encourage intermittent work. It encourages delay in starting operations because of contemplated speed. That, of itself, is a strong reason for sticking to the horses. It is the universal rule that steady work is better for the man and better for his business."[11]

Robbins later wrote a 30-page pamphlet published by the University of Illinois College of Agriculture in 1930 which discussed using larger hitches on the farms to boost production. The larger-hitch theory was thought by many to be fairly effective in convincing farmers that, if used more effectively, horses could still compete with the up-and-coming tractor industry. The large-hitch movement stayed alive as the Horse Association of America, later to become the Draft Horse and Mule Association of America, also promoted the large hitches as profitable.

Tractors curtail horse breeding

The proponents of the tractor industry continued to place doubts in the minds of American farmers regarding the usefulness of using horses for field work. Because many farmers were unsure of the horse's future, they curtailed and even suspended breeding operations. McFarland warned of an impending shortage again and again throughout the 1920s. This shortage spelt an excellent opportunity for farmers to sell young horses.

"Just now an actual shortage of horses appears to be on the way because breeding operations dwindled during the post-war agricultural depression. The equine population of the United States is now given as 14,541,000, the lowest in 40 years, and registers a decline of 25 percent in the past eight years. In 1919 there were 91 colts foaled per 1,000 horses and mules on farms and ranges in the United States, and in 1927 the number had dwindled to 42.4. This foaling rate is far below the replacement level.

"Such a situation cannot be remedied in a short time. At the present foaling rate it will take 23 years to replace our supply of work animals. Every colt will not live, and 15 years (is) a liberal estimate

of the average life of a horse. Young breeding stock is already scarce, and the outlook for the sale of colts is particularly good.

"There is also a ready market for Percheron geldings. City buyers have paid as much as $800 this year for a well matched pair in the favored color for geldings, dark gray. They want big, sturdy, dependable, and attractive horses, and Percherons fill the bill."[12]

For the most part, McFarland was right. The 1930s saw a slight revival in the use and raising of draft horses. Draft horse breeders who stayed in the business made some money. But more and more breeders realized that the end was near.

The 1930 United States Census revealed that the American farmer had indeed endorsed the Percheron as the preferred purebred draft horse. There were 235 Suffolks, 1,454 Clydesdales, 1,506 Shires, 8,841 Belgians and 33,033 Percherons in the United States, according to the 1930 U.S. Census, Association Secretary Ellis McFarland reported in 1937.

"These figures are an excellent answer to the question as to which breed is best suited for the American farmer. For ordinary purposes of comparison, all draft breeds have been in this country about the same length of time. Therefore, since there are almost three times as

Photo Courtesy of J.C. Allen & Son

Photographs like this one, emphasizing the breed's gentleness, were used to lure people to the Percheron.

many registered Percherons in this country as there are Belgians, Clydesdales, Shires, and Suffolks combined, it is easy to see which breed the American farmer prefers.

"Percherons constitute half of all registered horses in the U.S. including light horses." [13]

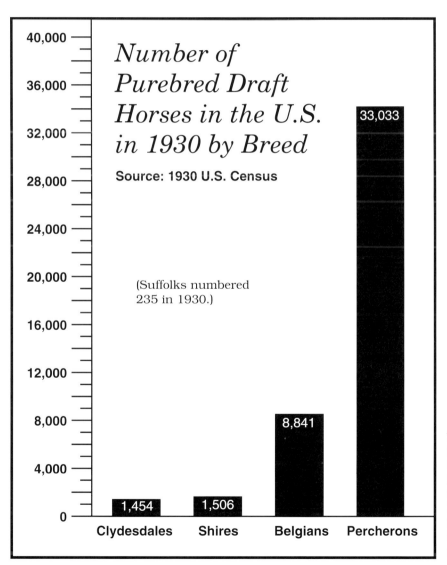

Number of Purebred Draft Horses in the U.S. in 1930 by Breed

Source: 1930 U.S. Census

(Suffolks numbered 235 in 1930.)

Breed	Number
Clydesdales	1,454
Shires	1,506
Belgians	8,841
Percherons	33,033

There were almost three times as many registered Percherons in the U.S. as all other breeds combined in 1930, just as the draft horse industry was beginning to decline.

Percherons were preferred by farmers for a variety of reasons, according to McFarland:

"The Percheron has the widest appeal of any of the draft breeds as an all-around farm horse. The expression, attitude, and action of this strong and diligent draft horse suggest strength, energy, activity, robustness, and endurance. A mere glance shows how fine his muscular system is in proportion to his weight. He has clean limbs, strong joints, and excellent feet.

"The Percheron is the best balanced of the large breeds. Most Percherons are medium-sized, large enough to do any kind of work on a farm, but not so large as to be clumsy. They take a good sized load to town, and if the driver is in a hurry they trot back with the empty wagon. Too much trotting is not good for any drafter, but the Percheron will take more punishment than any of the other breeds. High tribute can be paid to American breeders for helping develop

Photo Courtesy of J.F. Abbernathy

The Percheron dominated the registered draft horse world when draft horses provided much of the world's power.

and perfect a draft horse which fills the farmer's needs in every section of this continent with its varied climates and farm conditions.

"The Percheron is by far the handiest on his feet of any of the draft breeds. His action is often credited with a Hackney-like quality. He is naturally an up-headed horse with a great deal of sense. His disposition has no equal. A study of his head is enough to indicate to any horseman his unusual intelligence. His neatly turned throatlatch indicates his ability to stand extremely high temperatures. It allows freer breathing than is possible in a low-headed, thick-necked, heavy-jawed horse.

"The Percheron breed has won the enviable reputation during the past few years of attracting into its ranks many businessmen who have reached the top in their professions.

"Lawyers, bankers, insurance men, manufacturers, dentists, railroad officials, physicians, surgeons, merchants, stock and bond brokers, newspaper officials, even men famous as entertainers on stage and radio, and men in other such varied fields of business, are buying farms near cities, particularly near larger cities. They are stocking these farms with registered Percheron mares to do work ordinarily done by grades."[14]

In the 1928 Percheron Review, Ellis McFarland published a collection of editorials written by several of the most successful Percheron breeders of the day entitled "Why We Like Percherons."

Photo Courtesy of Cook & Gormley

Frances McFarland, daughter of Society Secretary Ellis McFarland, holds two mares owned by Osborne and Aileen White of Healdsburg, Calif., which together weighed 3,700 pounds. Circa 1936.

One of the contributors was Fred Holbert who — with brother Tom — operated a very successful draft horse breeding operation in Greeley, Iowa. Because the Holberts were successful with Belgians and Shires as well as Percherons, Fred Holbert was an excellent source when comparing the Percheron to other breeds.

"As importers bringing over scores of shipments of Percheron stallions from France during the past 25 years and as shippers of thousands of Percherons in this country, the great endurance and the hardiness of the Percheron has been a great source of satisfaction to us.

"He has, in case of sickness, exceptional resistance and in my opinion no breed of horses will stand more grief and hardship than the Percheron, and I know of no horse that has more intelligence or a better disposition than has the Percheron.

"The Percheron is the ideal draft horse on our farms and for the heavy drays of the cities of this country.

"The Percheron is truly an all purpose horse."[15]

In the same issue, Alex Galbraith of Edmonton, Alberta, Canada, wrote why he felt the Percheron was the best breed of draft horse to be used on America's farms.

"Wherever one may choose to travel, he will find more Percheron horses by far than any other breed. This situation has never changed during the 40 odd years that I have been familiar with draft horse interests on this side of the Atlantic. If you ask a farmer why he prefers the Percheron to other draft breeds, he usually replies something like this: 'We like Percherons because they are gentle and easily broken,' or 'We prefer them because their legs are free from long hair and therefore are more easily cared for.' Some will say that they like them because they are better feeders and shippers or 'we find they are more popular among the horse buyers.' Others will admit that their preference for Percherons is due to the fact that they mature earlier than most of the other breeds and attain a good weight at an early age. It is not at all uncommon to hear a farmer say that he likes the beautiful dapple gray Percherons because the color was popular on the market, or black because they never turn white."[16]

Galbraith continued:

"So universal has been the use of the Percheron horse on American farms during the past 50 years, that the advocates or

salesmen representing other draft breeds were generally filled with something approaching dismay when they tried to dispose of stallions and mares of competing breeds almost anywhere in the United States. I can speak on this subject with a great deal of assurance and certainty begot from actual experience. At a period when I thought somewhat less of the Percheron breed than I do today, I sometimes tried to bring the merits of some other breeds in which I was interested to the attention of American farmers. I almost invariably found that the Percheron breed was so deeply imbedded in the affections of the farmers, both East and West, that it was the hardest kind of work to get them even partially interested in any other breed. These farmers showed me their stock, young and old, with pardonable pride. They told me of the sales made at handsome profits and declared their sincere admi-

A team of Percherons, one black, the other nearly white, pull a load of loose grass hay over a dirt road.

ration for the breed that had proved so satisfactory under all the various conditions existing. I do not believe candidly that any other breed of draft horses could have stood the test with equal satisfaction as the Percheron has done during the last century, and which still retains its wonderful hold over a large majority of American farmers today. To be exact, according to the last census report two-thirds of all the purebred draft horses owned in the United States were Percherons.

"After nearly 45 years of continuous admiration for America's favorite heavy drafter I am forced to conclude that as a farm horse and subject to existing conditions, I do not hesitate to give the Percheron breed the leading place." [17]

In the September 30, 1920 Breeder's Gazette, a New York farmer praised the value of keeping Percherons on the farm rather than mules or making the switch to tractor power:

"There is a farmer who raises and uses his own 'tractors.' He does not take too much stock in the statement that horses eat their heads off while they stand idle, because his are producing more 'tractors' while they are idle, and these in turn pay profits. He is no enemy of the farm tractor, but does say that there is considerable profit in horses for the farmer who selects good bloodlines and gives the animals work to do.

"A.J. Wempe of Marshall Co., Kans., makes big Percheron mares do all his farm work, and also produces registered stock for which there is a large demand. The farm has not had a gelding on it in the past ten years; neither has Mr. Wempe a tractor. Recently he reached out, adding a quarter-section (160 acres) to his quarter-section, and with one hired man and his own son he continues, with his purebred mares, to supply the power needed to operate the farm with profit.

"'I have been using four-horse teams for the heavier farm work,' Mr. Wempe confided. 'It has worked satisfactorily for years. Last summer I was plowing during the dry weather when my neighbor, just across the fence, who was using a light tractor, was forced to quit. The mares are gentle and my 11-year-old son has been helping me cultivate the last two years. One would not dare to put a nine-year-old up behind a span of mules.'

"Mr. Wempe said that he recognized the value of a sound mule as a farm animal. 'But one can buy a team of big mares almost for the price of a mule,' he explained. 'If a mule loses an eye, or is cut

badly in wire, it depreciates rapidly in value. A brood mare, despite these accidents, can still produce registered offspring.'"[18]

For the most part, World War II postponed the inevitable.

But by 1948, it had become clear to even the staunchest supporters of the Percheron breed, that the days of horsedrawn agriculture were over. The Percheron breed, which had provided much of the power to fuel the industrial and agricultural expansion of America, declined rapidly in numbers.

Throughout the 1950s, '60s and early '70s, the Percheron industry suffered its worst years. Only a handful of dedicated Percheron breeders remained. The 1980s, however, saw a renewed interest in Percherons and draft horses in general. Were it not for those few breeders who had stayed the course and maintained breeding herds during the hard times there would never have been a reservoir of Percheron horses to meet the increased demand of the 1980s, and the breed would almost surely have been lost.

Photo Courtesy of Michigan State University

This Percheron team hauled the large tub used for emptying the maple buckets at Michigan State College.

The remaining chapters of this book discuss the origin of the Percheron breed in Europe, the breed's emigration to the United States, the history of the American Percheron Association from its formation in 1876 up to 1990, and some of the more prominent figures in the history of the breed.

References

[1] Will Brock, letter published in part in *Circus Baggage Stock*, by Charles Philip Fox, 1983, p. 5.

[2] *Circus Baggage Stock*, Charles Philip Fox, Heart Prairie Press, Box 332, Whitewater, WI 53190, 1983.

[3] Wayne Dinsmore, "The Outlook for Draft Horse Breeding," The Percheron Review, (1916), p. 2.

[4] United States Department of Foreign and Domestic Commerce

[5] "Survey Shows 7,941 Percherons Imported into United States Over 28 Year Period," Percheron News, (October, 1939), p. 24.

[6] Dinsmore, "The Outlook for Draft Horse Breeding," The Percheron Review, (1916), p. 4.

[7] Dinsmore, "War's Problems for Horse Breeders," The Percheron Review, (1917), p. 2.

[8] D.F. Houston, "A Word to Horsemen," The Percheron Review, (1917), p. 2.

[9] Dinsmore, "The Future of Draft Horse Production," The Percheron Review, (1917), p. 3.

[10] E.T. Robbins, "The Farm Horse Situation," The Percheron Review, (1923), p. 5.

[11] Ibid.

[12] Review, 1929, p. 1.

[13] Ellis McFarland, 1937 National Percheron Show Premium List & History, Percheron Horse Association of America, Chicago, August, 1937, p. 50.

[14] Ibid., p. 54.

[15] Fred Holbert, Why We Like Percherons, The Percheron Review, Percheron Association of America, Chicago, 1928, p. 17.

[16] Review, 1928, p. 5-7.

[17] Ibid., p. 19.

[18] Breeder's Gazette, Sept. 30, 1920, p. 622.

A Breed Born of Battle

The Origin of the Percheron

A Breed Born of Battle

(732 - 1840)

The question of the Percheron Breed's origin is largely academic. The breed, as it has been known in America for the past 100 years, must differ dramatically from its early roots — whatever they may be. It is now a unique and individual breed, the product of centuries of breeding practices to emphasize the animal's desirable qualities.

Those admired qualities changed over time. In the Middle Ages, the ancestor of the Percheron was used little as a draft animal, but instead served as a war horse to carry knights into battle. Those horses were light (by comparison to Percherons of today), sure-footed and spirited. As the agricultural revolution continued, the horses took to the wheat and barley fields more often than the battlefield and were bred more for size, weight and strength.

According to most experts, this selective breeding took place in France, especially within the Perche district. Le Perche consists mostly of undulating country, interrupted with small valleys with good pasture bottoms. Its climate is temperate. The clay soil and limestone base "undoubtedly has contributed to the Percheron's excellent bone."[1]

While the question of the breed's early roots matters little, if any, in discussing the breed in modern America today, an examination of the breed's more recent history should include some historical perspective.

The French developed the breed but made little effort to document its history. Or if they had documented it, those records have not survived, according to Alvin Sanders and Wayne Dinsmore:

"They have developed the Percheron horse, but his real origin is involved in almost total obscurity. Only speculation can be indulged in concerning his remote past, and strange to relate, until

now few facts have been available touching the evolution during the past (19th) century of the heavy draft type, which, it must be understood, is a modern creation."[2]

It is widely speculated that among the horses used by the French for horse breeding were a number of Arabian desert horses. The French captured these horses after turning back invasions by the Moslems and other nations of the East. The best known of these battles occurred in 732 A.D. when Charles Martel, King of Old France, overcame the Moslem army between Tours and Poitiers of central France.

"That Arab blood was left behind at the time of this crowning disaster to Oriental arms in western Europe no one need doubt; and looking down the long vista of the centuries that have come and gone since then, we may find in this a possible explanation of

The Percheron draft horse was born out of war. During battle, the French captured their enemies' horses, later breeding them to French stock to develop war horses for France.

the combined style and substance of the gray and white chargers so numerous in the middle ages — a possible cross of the eastern blood-horse upon a weightier western type."[3]

Some ten centuries later, more Arabian blood was likely infused with the domestic horses of France during the latter part of the

The first Arabian horses to have been bred with French horses were captured by the French army after routing attacks by Moslem armies in the Eighth Century.

Middle Ages when Crusaders invaded the Holy Land, according to Sanders and Dinsmore:

"It has been said that the Perche received liberal introductions of Arabian blood following the return of the Crusaders, who are alleged to have brought back stallions that were freely used to the great profit of the horses of the district.

"It is further alleged that while the blood was also brought into other provinces it was nowhere so carefully conserved or in-bred as in the Perche. All of which may be true, or it may be pure invention."[4]

The French presumably bred these Arabian horses to their own stock to develop horses better suited to serve in battle during the Middle Ages.

"The horse that could serve successfully the purposes of the mail-clad warriors of feudal times had to be up to carrying a lot of weight. With the burdens put upon them, no weakling steeds would long survive the shock of joust or tournament or the more serious work of the field of battle. Not only was the charger himself sometimes loaded down with his own gear — metal-ornamented caparison, with perchance steel breast-plate and head-piece — but in the saddle was an athletic rider with his load of iron and lance or battleaxe in place. Substance without sluggishness was a prime consideration. Activity in hand-to-hand combat meant losing or gaining all. A horse with proud carriage was demanded to meet the state and dignity of nobility and royalty. In brief, only a grand good type of horse could meet the imperative requirements of those whose lives depended so largely upon the weight and mettle of their mounts."[5]

A third infusion of Arabian blood may have occurred when, in 1760, "the royal stud at Le Pin made Arab stallions available to local (Percheron) breeders."[6]

The French Revolution nearly spelled the end of the Percheron breed. From the start of the revolution in 1789 to the early 1800s, horse breeding was suspended and suppressed. When breeding later resumed, another Arabian influence was said to have occurred. Two Le Pin Arabian stallions, Godolphin and Gallipoly, were allegedly used to help the breed recover.[7] Most books documenting the Percheron horse history include the stallions Godolphin and Gallipoly as having significantly influenced the breed around 1820. The first known documentation of these horses' influence is found in a book by M. Chas. du Hays, who remains one of the breeds most distinguished early historians. Using Hays' work without questioning its accuracy, other writers perpetuated the Godolphin and Gallipoly influence as fact. Hays claimed that:

"These two valuable stock-getters (Godolphin and Gallipoly), both gray, again gave tone and ardor to the Percheron race, and transformed definitely into gray horses the stock of the entire country, which had, it is said, become less uniform, and of all colors."[8]

Upon closer examination, it was found that the two animals were neither both Arabians nor both gray. Godolphin was an unremarkable saddle horse, probably Arabian, and chestnut in color. During an inspection in 1812, the horse was found to have the following characteristics: "Conformation ordinary; hocks bad and straight; ugly croup; he trots badly."[9] Gallipoly was a "speckled gray saddle stallion barely 15 hands high. He was not an Arab and scarcely the type, one would say, to build up the Percherons around 1820, among which there were many big approved gray stallions in actual service and founding the modern draft type from within the limits of the native breed itself."[10]

Alvin Sanders and Wayne Dinsmore reported Du Hay's error in their book, *A History of the Percheron Horse,* and added that the writers who had perpetuated the story should not be held at fault for doing so: "The story was given currency by a writer who knew and loved the Percheron, and who would not knowingly mislead anybody in respect to their derivation. There was none to deny or disprove it."[11] Sadly, the myth remains as several books about draft horses, many written in the last forty years, continue to cite the Godolphin and Gallipoly influence with surety.

The foreword to the 25th volume of the Percheron Stud Book of America — written by longtime Percheron breeder and Percheron Association Director James M. Barnhart in the early 1980s — credits Sanders with refuting the Arab influence entirely. In fact, Sanders simply discounted the Godolphin and Gallipoly influence but clearly stated that earlier infusions of Arabian blood had almost definitely occurred.

Sanders and Dinsmore assert that enough good Percherons

survived the tumultuous period at the onset of the 19th Century to assist the breed's recovery. These writers maintained the modern Percheron, in essence, already existed.

The development of the French draft horse continued — but from within. Buyers began demanding larger horses. Horses from other districts in France were being used to enlarge the horse of the Perche district from a 1,200 to 1,400 pound coach horse to a 2,000 pound drafter.

As the French draft horses became more popular among buyers, some horses were being labeled as Percherons, some Normans, and others were simply called French draft horses. The need of establishing common guidelines for breed requirements was beginning to be felt in France, but it was the U.S. Percheron breeders who first dealt officially with the subject in 1876, seven years before their French counterparts.

Except for the recent past, the history of the Percheron breed is muddled. Few clear, unrefutable facts exist. But whatever their distant origin, horses called Percherons began arriving in the U.S. in the mid nineteenth century to eventually became the most popular breed of draft horse in the United States.

Sixteenth Century France is depicted in this engraving.

References

[1]Valerie Russell, *Heavy Horses of the World*, (Northants, England: Country Life Books, 1983), p. 70.

[2]Alvin Howard Sanders and Wayne Dinsmore, *A History of the Percheron Horse*, (Sanders Publishing Co., 1917), p. 34.

[3]Ibid., p. 37.

[4]Ibid., p. 38.

[5]Ibid., p. 40.

[6]Valerie Russell, *Heavy Horses of the World*, (Northants, England: Country LIfe Books, 1983), p. 70.

[7]Ibid., p. 70.

[8]Charles du Hays, *The Percheron Horse*, (New York, NY: The Art Age Press, 1886), p. 33.

[9]Alvin Howard Sanders and Wayne Dinsmore, *A History of the Percheron Horse*, (Sanders Publishing Co., 1917), p. 63.

[10]Ibid., p. 64.
[11]Ibid., p. 67.

Arriving in the New World

The First Percherons Come to the United States

The First Percherons
Come to the United States

(1850 - 1880)

While some French horses of the draft horse type found their way to the United States in the first half of the nineteenth century, the first true Percheron type to have been imported is credited to Edward Harris, of Moorestown, N.J. While on vacation in northern France, Harris "became so impressed with the excellence of the hardy horses that hauled the heavy diligences in which he traversed the country that he determined to ship a few specimens to the United States."[1]

Edward Harris of New Jersey was among the first to successfully import Percherons from France to the United States. Harris' first importation attempt occurred in 1839.

Harris' first attempt in 1839 proved mostly unsusuccessful as only one of the four he imported survived the voyage, and that was a mare. He immediately tried again, this time bringing two stallions and two mares, one of which died shortly after arriving in the states. Of the stallions, one went blind his first year in the U.S. and was retired from service. One of the mares — whether from the first shipment or the second, it is unknown — proved unable to breed, and so after purchasing eight horses to import to America, only two, a mare named Joan and a stallion called Diligence, were able to help establish the Percheron breed here.[2]

Diligence was described as a compactly built horse standing about 15 hands. According to his owner he begot about 400 foals before his death in 1856. Three of his progeny, a mare named Julie and two stallions, Diligence 2d and Louise Philippe, were recorded among the foundation animals accepted for registry in the first American Percheron stud book in 1876.

No other importations from France are on record until 1851 when three stallions were imported, Normandy 351, Louis Napoleon 281 and a horse named Gray Billy.

Normandy

Normandy 351 was purchased as a coming three-year-old in France by Dr. Brown of Circleville, Ohio, in 1851. Brown had little success promoting the horse in Ohio and eventually sold him to Bigelow & Marshall of Pleasant Valley, Ohio, where the

Normandy 351, or Pleasant Valley Bill as he was later called, was imported in 1851 by Dr. Brown in Circleville, Ohio where the horse helped promote the Percheron breed among horsemen there.

stallion "achieved a splendid reputation, begetting an amazingly numerous progeny."[3] The first volume of the American Percheron Stud Book stated that Normandy, or Pleasant Valley Bill as he was then known, "did more than any other in that locality to enhance the popularity of the 'French horses,' as they were generally called in Central Ohio. He was a very sure foal getter and is known to have got one hundred and ten colts in one season."

Normandy never weighed over 1,500 pounds and was about 15.5 hh., "considerably below the average size of the Percheron-Normans that are usually imported to America." His progeny were "remarkable for their uniformity, none being very large, but all of them large enough for good, general-purpose horses."[4]

Gray Billy

The coach horse colt called Gray Billy was imported by Samuel Holman of Phoenixville, Penn., and accompanied Normandy 351 and Louis Napoleon 281 from France to New York in 1851. Samuel's son, Lewis E. Holman related in 1917 the history of the horse in Sanders and Dinsmore's *A History of the Percheron Horse:*

Gray Billy accompanied Normandy 351 from France to New York in 1851 where he was then transported to the Holman Farm in Pennsylvania.

"Gray Billy, as we called our horse, was shipped to the home of my father's brother, Frederic Holman, to await my father's arrival. From there he was brought to our farm on which we still live and always have lived. The reason we do not know his age when he died is that after keeping him many years we sold him to a Mr. Bird of New Jersey. How long he lived after that we do not know. His weight was between 1,300 and 1,400 pounds. His colts were fine and he was a sure foal-getter. He was not popular at first, but it was not long before he was appreciated, though not in our immediate neighborhood. Buyers came from New York and many places of distance to buy his colts as they were remarkably fine and far superior to the colts by ordinary horses. He was a dark silver, dappled, three years old, one year older than Valley Bill (Normandy 351). He was perfectly gentle and for his size very active, as were all of his colts."

Louis Napoleon

The other major 1851 importation was of the three-year-old colt Louis Napoleon 281 by three Ohio men — Erastus Martin and Pearl Howard, both of Woodstock, and James Fullington of Milford Center. While visiting France, Martin saw a large gray stallion and was determined to buy him. His efforts were un-successful, however, so "he did the next best thing and bought a three-year-old full brother described at that time as 'a raw,

Louis Napoleon was perhaps the most successful breeding stallion of his day. He serviced record numbers of mares of which most, sadly, were of mixed breeding.

unfinished colt' but promising to attain good size." That horse was Louis Napoleon.

Upon arrival in the states, "the chunky, short-legged, grey colt and his importers were the butt of every horseman's joke in the country." In his first year, Louis Napoleon bred only ten mares, seven of which belonged to his owners. Yet, within two years, after his offspring began to "show signs of that remarkable excellence that was destined soon to make the despised French Horse famous throughout the entire West,"[5] those who publicly berated the animal began servicing their mares to him.

In 1854, the French Horse, as he became known, was purchased for $1,500 by A.P. Cushman of Dewitt, Co., Ill. Then in 1858, after a number of transactions were completed which traded several interests in the horse, a controlling interest was purchased by Ellis Dillon and his nephews, Isaiah and Levi Dillon. Louis Napoleon was then moved to Tazewell County, Ill., where the Dillons lived. He was sent to the farm of Eli Hodgson in Grand Ridge township, La Salle County, to stand during the fall where he was used on only seven mares. As his progeny began to become better developed and more publicized, however, interest began growing in the stallion:

Levi Dillon

"Early in the spring of 1860, the fast-whitening stallion was returned to the Dillon headquarters, and as his foals developed his business in the stud increased. By mid-summer the demand for his services had become pressing and great secrecy was maintained regarding the date at which he was to be moved again to the Hodgson farm in La Salle. Young Martin Hodgson rode the white horse home in the dead hour of the night following the celebration of the national holiday (July 4). But so keen has been the scouting that when the journey was ended at a little before dawn, it is related that

no less than forty-two mares were tied to the fences surrounding the Hodgson homestead awaiting their chance to be bred or booked. He had served but seven the season before."[6]

Because few, if any, horses bred to Louis Napoleon were purebred Percherons, the stallion's name is found in few contemporary Percheron pedigrees. He was, nevertheless, one of the animals which helped promote the Percheron-Norman breed in the United States.

The best crosses using Louis Napoleon were with descendants of the Dillons' Samson sire. Samson, probably a Shire,[7] was imported by Col. Charles Oakley in 1843 from England. In its infancy, the Percheron breed found one of its greatest champions in the Dillon family. Ellis Dillon served as the American Percheron-Norman Association's first president.

"The Dillons bred 28 stallions and 13 mares between 1871 and 1880, most of them produced after 1876. They bred some very high-class animals, especially in mares, were aggressive exhibitors in the showring and good advertisers, and by reason of their prestige and influence in central Illinois in a business and a political sense, they exerted a strong influence on draft horse breeding. They were not particular, however, to hold strictly to Percheron type and bought many useful horses of other French derivation. They emphasized great weight, massiveness, and ruggedness, and placed rather less importance upon quality, finish, and action."[8]

One of the most auspicious importers of the day, as well as one of the more effective promoters of the breed, was W.T. Walters of Baltimore, Md. In 1868, Walters imported four stallions and seven mares. He had a translation made of Charles du Hays' history of the Percheron horse and published the volume at his own expense in 1886. At least two editions were published. The first was a compact volume which included engravings secured by Walters of his horses. The second was an elaborate edition distributed among his friends "profusely illustrated with plates of (Walters)

W.T. Walters

stallions and mares made from photographs." Many copies of this second edition still exist and are the prized possessions of those who own them.

References

[1]Alvin Howard Sanders and Wayne Dinsmore, *A History of the Percheron Horse*, (Sanders Publishing Co., 1917), pp. 109-110.

[2]Ibid., p. 110.

[3]Ibid., p. 116.

[4]The Percheron-Norman Stud Book (America), Stock Journal Company, Chicago., 1978.

[5]Sanders and Dinsmore, p. 120.

[6]Ibid., p. 122.

[7]Ibid., p. 165.

[8]Ibid., p. 166.

A History of the Percheron Association of America

(1876 - 1991)

Birth Pains

(1876-1902)

The origin of the Percheron Horse Association of America can be traced back to a meeting held in Chicago in February, 1876, when fourteen men, representing three states, formed the "National Association of Importers and Breeders of Norman Horses." The group included Simon Ruble of Wisconsin, and Mark Dunham, Ellis, Levi and Isaiah Dillon, James Perry, W.J. Edwards, James Owen, and W.E. Prichard, all of Illinois. Also among the fourteen members was James H. Sanders of Illinois, considered by many to be the founder of livestock journalism. The following year, the group published the first U.S. stud book of the breed under the direction of James H. Sanders. A revised edition of this stud book was published in late 1878.

James Sanders (at right) formed his own publishing company based in Chicago and published the first true livestock journal, the *Western Stock Journal,* which eventually became the *National Livestock Journal.* His son, Alvin Sanders, served as editor of *The Breeder's Gazette,* the leading stock publication of its day, and co-wrote *A History of the Percheron Horse* with Wayne Dinsmore published in 1917.

Since Sanders was instrumental in compiling the first Percheron Stud Book, he also laid the groundwork for forming the American Percheron Association. His research on the subject of the breed's origin helped guide the association, from the start, to maintain standards of livestock integrity which would later be used as examples by other developing breed associations.

Percheron vs. Norman

While the official title of the association referred only to Norman horses, the name "Percheron-Norman Horses" was attached to the title of the Association's stud book by Sanders, despite instructions he received from the original fourteen members to use only the name "Norman Horses." In the preface of the original first edition of the stud book, Sanders explained his reasons for choosing the compound title:

"It will be noticed that I have departed from the recommendation of the meeting of breeders and importers of these horses, held in Chicago, in February, 1876, in the matter of the name by which these horses shall be known in America. So well satisfied have I become that almost all of the desirable qualities possessed by the French horses imported to America are due to the ancient Percheron race, that I have determined to adhere to that name, and to use it in connection with the term Norman, by which they have been extensively designated in this country."[1]

At the outset of the second meeting of the association in February, 1878, a number of members asked Sanders to further explain his reasons for the name change. His answer appears in the official report of the meeting:

"Mr. Sanders stated that when, in pursuance of an arrangement with this society, he actively set about the work of preparing a record of imported French draft horses, he fully intended to carry out the instructions of the society in reference to the name, but that he was met at the very threshold of his efforts by decided opposition upon that point. He found the use of the term Norman, as a name for this horse, confined exclusively to the West. The society which had inaugurated the enterprise comprised but fourteen members, and these nearly all resided in Central Illinois, while those interested in these horses were scattered throughout the United States and Canada. The Stud Book, to be of any service, must be such as to command the support of all sections. More than half of those who were interested designated these horses as Percherons. Those east

of Ohio used this term almost exclusively. In Ohio they were usually called French horses. In Illinois, Iowa, Wisconsin, and elsewhere in the West, breeders generally called them Percheron-Normans or Norman-Percherons in their advertisements, catalogues, etc., while the people in the West, in talking of them, almost universally called them Normans. In the literature of France they were always called Percherons, and so far as we had any literature in this country upon the subject, the same name was used. It was the breed universally known and designated in France as Percherons that gave name and fame to the French draft horses that are imported to the United States. In the introduction to the Stud Book he had set forth, as fully as he was able, the origin of this famous race of horses, and the relation which the modern French draft horse sustained to the ancient Percheron race. He had been very much disposed to drop the use of the term Norman entirely, and to call the book the Percheron Stud Book, and he read extracts from several recognized authorities recommending that course. But, on account of the previous action of this society, and the extent to which the word had been used by breeders and others in the West, either by itself or in combination with Percheron, he felt that its rejection would work an injury to such as had advertised their horses exclusively as Normans, and would tend to increase the prevalent confusion."[2]

Ellis Dillon

Isaiah Dillon, nephew of Ellis Dillon who presided over the meeting, said during the discussion that "many people used both names from policy. Some people wanted a Percheron horse, others wanted a Norman, not understanding the fact that they were substantially the same; and breeders and importers used both names, so that they could suit all classes of customers. It was the same in France. If a dealer found an American customer who wanted Percheron horses, he always had them; if he wanted Normans, why, that was just the kind of horse he had."[3]

At the same meeting, Daniel Dunham was elected president and B.H. Campbell was named Secretary.

Norman Name Dropped

The term Percheron-Norman stayed in use as the official title, despite the strong and vocal misgivings of Sanders and others, until November, 1883, when members of the association "unanimously voted that the word Norman should be dropped from the name of the society and its stud-book." The third volume of the American stud book was published in 1884 under the title of "The Percheron Stud Book of America" and included a preface by Sanders which, he undoubtedly hoped, would lay to rest the issue of what to call the French draft horse breed once and for all.

"In presenting this third volume to the public, I cannot refrain from expressing my gratification at the fact that the society under whose auspices the first volume was issued, in January, 1877, has at last, by a unanimous vote, decreed that the cumbersome and untruthful compound name Percheron-Norman, originally adopted in a spirit of compromise, should be abandoned, and that the name Percheron, which I had from the first advocated, as the only true name for this the most famous of all French breeds, should be used in its stead."[4]

Depression Hurts Percheron Industry

After its initial formation in 1876, the Percheron Horse Breeders Association of America enjoyed great success until financial depression struck the nation in 1891. From 1891 to 1900, Association business fell off as farmers bought and sold purebred Percheron horses as grades because they could not afford the cost of registering them. Although many of these horses were later registered after conditions improved,[5] during this period the association became less and less active.

In 1910, association President H.G. McMillan reminded his fellow members of what occurred during this depression period:

"You all remember the great depression in business that enveloped the country,

Isaiah Dillon

beginning near the first of the year 1893, and continuing until 1897 or 1898. During these years importations ceased. The breeders of horses in this country became discouraged. They could no longer sell their horses, even for market purposes, for sufficient (money) to give them compensation for their care and feed; and to sell them for breeding purposes was out of the question.

In consequence of this condition of affairs, interest seemed to be entirely lost in the Percheron organization, and the new idea of recording; and the establishment of stud books was neglected and almost forgotten. Finally, meetings were no longer held by the Society. There was no election of officers. Nobody paid any attention to the records, and finally, gentlemen, the condition became so serious that the secretary then in charge of the records, who endeavored to maintain them and keep them up, became so hard pressed for the necessary means to maintain the records, and an office to keep them in, that all the books of record were finally sold on execution, to pay the debts that were against the institution. Mr. S.D. Thompson, the last secretary elected, and who had charge of the records, bought the books and records at execution sale for a mere pittance, and became the absolute owner of all the property of the old organization."[6]

Samuel D. Thompson, who had been a respected associate of M.W. Dunham of Oaklawn Farm, Wayne, Ill., and an active secretary during the first years of the association, began calling his stud book the Thompson Stud Book.

Association Recovers

Shortly after 1900, when the nation's finances had begun to recover, many of the original members of The Percheron Horse Breeders Association came together and bought back the records from Thompson and — following a prolonged court battle — renamed the organization the American Percheron Horse Breeders and Importers Association in December, 1902.[7] The task of building up the association from virtual ruin lay in their hands.

References

[1] James H. Sanders, Preface to the First Edition of the Percheron-Norman Stud Book, The Stock Journal Company, Chicago, 1877.

[2] Minutes from the Second Meeting of the National Association of Importers and Breeders of Percheron-Norman Horses, Peoria, Ill., Feb. 14, 1878.

[3] Ibid.

[4] James H. Sanders, Preface to the Third Volume of the Percheron Stud Book of America, J.H. Sanders & Co., Chicago, 1884., p. 3.

[5] Barnhart, James M., "A Brief History of the Percheron Horse," Percheron Stud Book of America, Volume XXV, Percheron Horse Association of America, 1984, p. xvi.

[6] Minutes from the Eighth Annual Meeting of the Percheron Society of America held November 28, 1910, at the Unicorn Stock Yards, Chicago, Ill.

[7] Ibid.

Establishing Credibility

(1905-1910)

For the next several years, members of the American Percheron Horse Breeders and Importers Association worked to establish their association as the leading breed organization for the Percheron horse. Other breed registries had been established for French Draft and Norman horses, each classifying as French Draft and Norman the same horses the American Percheron Horse Breeders and Importers Association also deemed acceptable as Percherons.

President H.G. McMillan

Association is Renamed

On August 19, 1905, the U.S. Percheron association took another name — this time to The Percheron Society of America, the name by which the association was known for the next thirty years.

Challenges Ahead

The work ahead of this Society was great. Because the Percheron trade was again flourishing, and farmers and teamsters were again asking for registered Percherons, the role of the breed association continued to be more vital. Some breeders fraudulently applied for registered pedigrees for their grade (of mixed breeding) stock. Others were simply uninformed regarding the requirements for registering their horses as Percherons. The Percheron Horse Association spent the next five to six years establishing and defending its credibility.

The Breeder's Gazette ran the following letter from one of their Illinois subscribers and Society President H.G. McMillan's reply in their Jan. 19, 1910, issue in an attempt to clarify the breed issue:

Question:

"I have heard it claimed that the association now known as the Percheron Society of America, previous to the year 1894 registered animals with three or four top crosses. I have been told that in 1894 the laws of the association were revised so that they would take only animals whose sire and dam were purebred and registered, but would still continue to register animals that were the offspring to those already registered by being eligible by the three or four top crosses. Now I understand that there is an association called the National French Draft Horse Association, successor to the National Register of Norman Horses that would register five top crosses, but that none are eligible to registration by the Percheron Society of America except those having purebred sires and dams which were registered either by the Percheron Society of America or the French Percheron Society of France. Who is correct?"

Answer:

"The Percheron Society of America has never admitted anything for registration in its stud book unless the sire and dam were both recorded in either the Percheron Stud Book of France or the Percheron Stud Book of America. The old American Percheron Association under the Administration of S.D. Thompson did for a comparatively short time admit American bred animals upon a showing of five top crosses of registered sires, but the Percheron Society of America since its reorganization seven years ago has never accepted any registrations of this kind. I understand the rules of the National Register of Norman Horses, commonly known as the French Draft Book, accept registrations under the five top cross rule."[1]

What is a Percheron?

From the beginning, the question "What is a Percheron?" loomed overhead. With increasing demand for draft horses from American farmers — especially for the horses more people were calling Percherons — it was quite apparent to everyone that there was money to be made by whomever finally controlled the popular breed's registrations. The French Draft Horse Association was one of the last to give up to the Percheron Society of America. In 1910, Society President H.G. McMillan explained the difference between the French Draft Horse Association and the Percheron Horse Society of America:

"The difference between Percheron and the French Draft horses is not fully understood by many of our inquirers, the last of whom relates that there is considerable discussion in a Michigan neighborhood over this question. Some have gained the idea that the two names refer to one breed. This is a mistake. There are separate stud books for these breeds because those eligible to registry as French Drafters are not all eligible to registry as Percherons. Percherons include only the horses recorded in the Percheron stud books of France, Canada and the United States. The ancestors of the Percheron were found in the district of Le Perche, France, and only this foundation and its descendants are considered as Percherons. The horses of this district early became famous for their excellence and the attempt has been to preserve their superior qualities by preventing the introduction of outside blood. French Draft horses include those registered in the General Draft Horse Book of France and their descendants. These include Percherons and the several other draft breeds of France, some of which are considerably intermixed. The French Draft association does not recognize any difference between Percherons and the other draft horses of France, and admits Percherons to its records along with the other recorded draft horses descending from French stock. Only pure-bred Percherons may be recorded as Percherons, but they may also be recorded as French Drafters."[2]

During his opening address at the Seventh Annual meeting of the Percheron Society of America Nov. 29, 1909, Society President H.G. McMillan discussed the recent past of the Society:

"Most of you know that our organization, the one to which we now belong, was organized as a new institution, seven years ago this fall, and at that time we had nothing to work with except the interest and ambition and good will of our members.

"Subsequently we came into possession of the records of the old association; and I think there may be some misapprehension as to what our duties are, and what our obligations are, concerning the work of the past. When we came into possession of these old records we did the best we could with them. It should be kept in mind, however, that our association, and the membership of this association, was not responsible for the making of these records.

"Now, I do not wish to be understood as finding any fault with the old records, or saying they were not good records, or anything of that kind, but if there were errors and mistakes in those records we were not to blame for that.

"They were the only records that the Percheron breeders of America had, and they are the only records that they have today, except the ones that we have made since.

"Under the arrangement that was made at the time we came into possession of these records it was agreed that we would accept them as they were, in so far as they seemed to be regular on their face; that we would not undertake to change the records that had been made, but we would accept them in the form in which they came to us.

"We could not have changed them if we had tried. There was no way in which we could make any changes in these records. They were a matter of history and the business of the country had been done on the faith that was held in these records."[3]

Shortly after wrestling with the issue of establishing credibility and a sense of consistency at home, the Percheron Society of America also had to contend with reconciling their records with those of their colleagues overseas, McMillan continued:

"During all these years of depression in the draft horse industry, no stud books had been published either in this country or France. No stud book was published by Mr. Thompson for a period of about ten years, and when he did publish his volume, in 1898, he only gave the name of the horse recorded, with its number, and the name and number of the sire and dam. There was no extended pedigree so that it could be traced and compared with any published record.

"From 1894 until 1906, a period of twelve years, the Percheron Society of France did not publish a book, so that during this period of twelve years (in the past six of which, large importations were made, and distributed all over the United States) we absolutely had no means of verifying the pedigrees, and knowing whether they were accurate or not.

Secretary George Stubblefield

"The only thing we had was the certificate that was furnished our secretary, when the importer recorded his horse in this country. We could not tell whether that corresponded to the records of the French Society or not, because there were no published volumes during this period.

"It is a matter of history that the Percheron Society of France had three different secretaries during this time, all of whom are now dead, the last one dying, as I understand, prior to the publication of the volume in 1906.

"When this volume was published, comparisons were made between the records of France and the records here, and many discrepancies were discovered."[4]

U.S. Department of Agriculture Raises Questions

Because of these discrepancies and what was called the "'85 rule," the Percheron Society of America found itself with still another problem — this time with the U.S. Department of Agriculture. The "'85 rule" provided "that any animal that had been imported prior to or during 1885, regardless or whether it was recorded in the Percheron Stud Book of France or not, if the fact could be shown that the animal was really imported prior to that date, the horse was accepted for record in the American Stud Book."[5] The rule was developed, partly, because the French Stud Book was not established until 1883, long after a great many Percherons had been imported to the U.S.

"A year ago we were called to Washington by the Agricultural Department to explain some of these discrepancies. They cited us a considerable list of these imported horses, and also a number of American bred horses, that seemed to the department to have been recorded in our stud book without sufficient data."[6]

Most of the horses in question by the Agricultural Department had been recorded in Thompson's stud book and later also registered in the Society's stud book. After the histories of the two breed registries were explained to them, "they (federal agricultural officials) seemed fully satisfied," said McMillan.

But the agriculture officials were more difficult to satisfy in regard to the the discrepancies between the stud book of France and the Society's stud book.

"The Department of Agriculture seemed to think that it was our duty to, in some way, harmonize our records with the records of

the Percheron Society of France. We came home and undertook to see what could be accomplished along this line.

"We went at the work in good faith and made every effort to trace out these pedigrees that were called into question. The directors of the Percheron Society of America, and its officers, instituted a thorough investigation of all the matters involved. All records of every kind and character obtainable including original applications, the record books of our predecessors, and the stud books of all affiliated associations, were carefully and thoroughly examined and checked up. In addition, information was obtained by correspondence, and otherwise, from all available sources, for the purpose of securing evidence concerning the registration of all animals that were called in question. An extended correspondence was carried on with parties in all parts of the country, who might have knowledge as to these original transactions, and much information was obtained.

"In a large number of cases, the original certificates of pedigree were secured. In all cases where it was possible to find the

Photo Courtesy of Philip Weber

A team of dapple gray Percherons pulled this ice delivery wagon on the streets of Rockford, Ill., in 1908.

original certificates of pedigree, they were proved to be genuine and properly issued, under the seal of the society, and they bore the signatures of the proper officers."[7]

After diligently examining a number of the pedigreed Percherons under question in the U.S., Society officers concluded that "these certificates that were not recorded in the Percheron Stud Book of France were entitled to as much credit as any of the other certificates."[8]

The Society then "took the matter up with the Percheron Society of France, with a view of having them give recognition to these certificates that had been omitted from their published volumes, and endeavored to have the Society of France publish them in subsequent volumes. In the great majority of cases which we submitted to them, they adopted our suggestion, and propose to publish these pedigrees in their subsequent volumes."[9]

Six purebred Percherons plowing on an Indiana farm.

Photo Courtesy of J.C. Allen & Son

Shortly after reconciling the two nations' stud books, the American Percheron Society was again called before the U.S. Department of Agriculture — this time because "that, in addition to the pedigrees that had been called to our attention last year, the customs records as kept at Washington, and which had recently been checked up, disclosed that a considerable number of horses that had been recorded in our stud books did not appear upon the customs records."[10]

"But when we made our investigation, we found that the practice of the customs officers was to accept certificates from importers with but little question, and with practically no inspection or identification of the horses imported; that in consequence importers in many cases had been somewhat careless. If for any reason when they came to ship their horses to America, through oversight or error the seller brought the wrong certificates of pedigree, they would accept the pedigrees, bringing them with them, until their horses had passed the port of entry. They would then send them back and get the right certificates, and the correct certificates would be recorded in our books. The records at Washington, however, would show the certificates upon which the horses came through the port of entry.

"As a matter of fact, so far as we were able to discover, there was no attempt on the part of importers to take any advantage of the government. In many cases the horses being imported were in charge of men who could not read the foreign language, and they would not know whether they had the right pedigrees or not, when they were handed to them at the time of shipment."[11]

While the American Percheron Society was able to withstand the repeated attacks on its authenticity, the constant questioning of the validity of its pedigree certificates did damage to the reputation of the Society and to registered Percheron horse breeding in general, said McMillan.

"The American breeder should be absolutely secure and fully protected when he relies upon such certificate of pedigree in his breeding operation. If doubt should ever be entertained as to the correctness or reliability of pedigrees issued under such circumstances, the breeding interests of America would constantly be involved in great uncertainty, and no dealer or breeder in America would ever be safe when investing his money in breeding stock.

"The very basis of the Percheron Stud Book of America is the certificates of pedigree issued by the Percheron Stud Book of France. Our whole superstructure, and all our breeding interests in America rest upon these pedigrees, and necessarily any attack upon the pedigrees that we have heretofore recognized and published in our stud book, is a blow at the very foundation of all breeding operations in this country.

"Animals to which these pedigrees belong have passed from hand to hand, from stud to stud, involving hundreds of their progeny. Any action taken at this late day, by the Percheron Society of America, or the Department of Agriculture, that would unsettle or overthrow these pedigrees, would mean a loss of hundreds of thousands of dollars to the innocent American farmer and breeder."[12]

This Percheron, which looks remarkably similar to the Percheron found in the United States in modern times, served on the streets of Paris in 1908.

Society Makes Recommendations

In hopes of eliminating discrepancies between the records of the U.S. Customs Department and the American Percheron Society, the Society proposed a number of recommendations:

"We recommend that the Department of Agriculture establish a system of inspection of all imported horses; that the inspector be appointed as the direct representative of the Department of Agriculture, and that it shall be his duty carefully to examine and inspect all imported horses before passing the port of entry of this country for the following purposes:

"First: That it may be accurately ascertained and determined whether or not such horses have authentic certificates of pedigree from a reliable pedigree association in the country from which they come.

"Second: That such horses be inspected as to their identity, for the purpose of ascertaining whether or not they are correctly described in the pedigrees of the said horses, and also for the purpose of determining whether or not said pedigrees are genuine and duly authenticated.

"Third: That it may be determined whether or not such horses are free from dangerous, infectious and contagious diseases and suitable for improving purposes in this country.

"We further recommend that when inspection has been made, as herein provided, that an accurate and careful report of all imported horses, with the results of that inspection, be kept and made a matter of record in the Agricultural Department of the United States, for the information of all American Record Associations interested in the breed of horses; and that when information concerning such record and inspection of horses is requested by this society or any other having an interest in the same, it be furnished with as little delay as possible.

"We further recommend that the Department of Agriculture communicate with the Department of Agriculture of the Republic of France, or the Percheron Society of France, for the purpose of impressing upon said Percheron Society the importance of having authentic pedigrees, and a correct record made in the Percheron Stud Book of France, of all horses imported to this country, in order that no conflict may hereafter arise in the published records of the stud book of the Percheron Society of America, and the stud book of the Percheron Stud Book of France."[13]

The Society submitted their recommendations to the Agricultural Department which subsequently declined to adopt any of the proposals. In response, the Society appointed its own inspector "who was sent to the port of entry at New York, for the purpose of doing the work we had hoped the government might do. Our inspector has been in charge of this work ever since and has rendered splendid service, we believe."[14]

Not long after the Society named its own inspector, however, the U.S. government chose to adopt the recommendations after all, beginning January 1, 1911.

"They (U.S. Department of Agriculture) concede, as we claim, that it is the duty of the government to pass upon foreign certificates at the time the horses are entered at the customs office, and that they have no legal authority to hold us responsible for this work. They, therefore, propose to do all of this work in the future, and will inspect the horses, identify them, and pass upon their pedigrees, relieving us from that responsibility which in the past has caused us so much trouble."[15]

Society is Attacked from Within

But the Society's troubles continued. The Pedigree Committee of the Society worked earnestly to verify the authenticity of the pedigree applications.

"They have put in days, and weeks and I might say, almost, months, going through these applications, tracing them out, comparing them with former records, and seeing whether they are correct or otherwise.

"They have traveled hundreds, and I may say, thousands of miles, to take evidence bearing upon the facts, in order that they might ascertain the truth about these registrations. In a great many cases they have turned down applications and refused to accept them, not so much because they thought the men were dishonest who had made them, but because the evidence upon which they were based was not sufficient, in their judgement, to justify the recording of the animals covered by them."[16]

In the fall of 1911, the Pedigree Committee — consisting of three directors, W.E. Prichard, J.L. DeLancey and A. P. Nave — reported to the Society Board of Directors that:

"For the past seven months, systematic attacks have been made on the Percheron Society of America and its officers. These attacks

have been made public through certain papers, edited by parties who are avowedly hostile to the policies of the Percheron Society of America.

"Your Pedigree Committee, in the discharge of its duty, under the By-laws of the Society, has made a thorough investigation of these attacks and the reasons for the same. The results of the investigation of your Committee show that the attacks or charges made are either based upon typographical errors and technical mistakes, or are false and untrue.

"The investigations made by your Committee also show that the parties responsible for these attacks do not have the welfare of the Percheron Society of America at heart, but that the underlying motive is the desire to gain control of the management of the Percheron Society of America. The men responsible for the attacks are G.W. Patterson, William Danforth, G.L. Carlson and F.B. Graham, and the avowed purpose of these men is to break down and destroy the present Percheron organization."[17]

In response to the charges against their organization, the Society's Pedigree Committee referred to the recent investigation by McMillan and other Society officers into the validity of Society pedigrees:

"Your Committee would call attention to the fact that the Board of Directors, after the most careful consideration and after making a thorough examination of all the original records, applications and other data that could be obtained, reached the conclusion that in most cases these pedigrees were genuine and issued in good faith, having the signature of the proper officers and the seal of the Society, in all cases where it was possible to obtain the original certificates.

"The board deemed it wise and in fact absolutely necessary that all of these

Special Report of the Pedigree Committee

═══════ TO THE ═══════

BOARD OF DIRECTORS

═══════ OF THE ═══════

Percheron Society of America

Regarding Published Charges Concerning the Society

ISSUED OCTOBER 3rd, 1911, CHICAGO, ILLINOIS
BY ORDER OF THE BOARD

The Pedigree Committee filed this report with the Board of Directors October 3, 1911.

original records should be confirmed and left undisturbed; and after the hearing at Washington a year ago last June, the Department of Agriculture accepted the recommendations made by this Society, and soon thereafter the only other Society of recognized standing, competing with the Percheron Society of America, joined hands with our Society and for the first time in the recent history of Percheron registrations, we have a united and practically unanimous body of Percheron breeders in the United States.

"As evidence that the breeders of the country believe in this Association, we cite the fact that since our last annual meeting, more than 1,150 breeders have become members of the Percheron Society of America, bringing our total membership to more than 4,000 individual breeders who are actively engaged in breeding and distributing America's greatest draft horse.

"It is therefore to be regretted that a very few jealous and dissatisfied members, in an attempt to gain some personal advantages, should endeavor to destroy and break down what has been built up during the past nine years by the Percheron Society."[18]

Committee Member J.L. DeLancey

In the same report, the Pedigree Committee answered many allegations made by G.W. Patterson and others against the Society:

"It would be impracticable for this Committee in the space of this report, to go over, in detail, all of the various charges that have been made and to enter into detailed explanations of the various matters that attention is called to in the records of the Society.

"As heretofore stated, the parties responsible for the published attacks upon the Society, in order to accomplish their purpose, have relied upon calling attention to typographical errors and technicalities in the published volumes and have endeavored to make much capital out of same, when the most casual examination of the original records in the office of the Society would show their inferences and conclusions to be false. They have also resorted to the use of apparently false and fraudulent testimony."[19]

Enemies Make Charges of Fraud Against President

The report went on to discuss five widely publicized cases where typographical errors which occurred in the newly-published Percheron Stud Book were used by Patterson and his associates to discredit the Association. Among the five cases, one particularly singled out a Society officer, President H.G. McMillan:

"Besides attempting to create prejudice against the Society and its officers by calling attention to technical errors, the men responsible for the attacks have, to the best of our knowledge, resorted to securing false and fraudulent statements, and the publication of the same, in their attempts to arouse hostile public sentiment toward the Society and its officers. A specific case, which shows an attempt to falsely attach blame to a member of our board, follows:

"G.W. Patterson and his attorney went to Sylvester Egan of Humboldt, South Dakota, about June 6, 1911, and secured his signature to two statements which they drew. Said statements appear to have been secured from Egan by their promise to protect him from prosecution. These signed statements were apparently furnished to one of the two papers in which attacks have been published, and were published on September 1st, 1911."[20]

The case involving Sylvester Egan centered around two young horses Egan sold to McMillan in April, 1911. The horses were both unregistered and were the offspring of unregistered sires and dams. In an unofficial statement made by Egan dated June 6, 1911, Egan stated he was induced by McMillan to "put papers on the colt, as you have full blood mares (on your farm)."[21]

Charges are Found to Be False

After investigating the matter, the Pedigree Committee concluded that the statements made by Egan were false and were solicited from him by Patterson and his attorney under pressure.

Committee Member A.P. Nave

The Committee directed Egan to make a sworn affidavit:

"I, Sylvester Egan, on oath, state that I live in Buffalo Township, Minnehaha County, South Dakota. My attention being called to a statement signed by me dated June 6, 1911, and published in the Stallion and Jack News under the date of September 1, 1911. I desire to say with reference to said published statement that the latter part thereof is incorrect and untrue, in which I am made to say that H.G. McMillan asked me if I could not 'put papers on the colt, as you have full blood mares.' And wherein I was made to say that 'I did not represent the colt to be full blood, but I hastily, and on his (Mr. McMillan's) suggestion, signed an application for registering said colt as a full blood.'"

Egan explained that two weeks prior to meeting with McMillan, he had filled out registration papers for the two colts he knew were grades and sent them to the association. The papers were approved and sent back to Egan who subsequently sent them on to McMillan.

Egan added that Patterson and his attorney, E.H. Canfield induced Egan to sign the statement which appeared in The Stallion and Jack News by telling him he was "liable for serious prosecution" and that if he signed, Patterson and his attorney would protect him from prosecution.[22]

Patterson Makes New Charges

In addition to the Egan affair, McMillan was also accused by Patterson of misappropriating money used to defend himself against charges by the U.S. Department of Agriculture. Patterson was referring to the meetings between Society officers and the U.S. Department of Agriculture already discussed in this section.

"The truth is that a complaint was filed by the Department of Agriculture at Washington, alleging irregular registrations of some 283 horses, a number of which were imported horses. In the entire list that was involved, President McMillan was only interested in three and these were horses he had not bred or recorded himself.

"By direction of the Board, a Committee was appointed to go to Washington and take charge of this case. The Committee being composed of the following Directors: H.G. McMillan, C.O. Keiser, J.C. Robison, C.M. Jones, J.L. Delancey and A.P. Nave. By a resolution of the Board, the expenses of the Committee were paid by the Society. At the hearing at Washington, McMillan was simply paid actual expenses the same as the other Directors on the

Committee. The hearing resulted in a complete vindication of the position taken by the Society, and as heretofore stated, the recommendation made at the hearing by the Percheron Society was adopted by the Agricultural Department."[23]

Patterson Charged With Fraud

Finally, Patterson also publicized widely an injunction he had successfully served on the Directors of the Percheron Society in September, 1911. The injunction stemmed from an investigation by the Society into allegations that Patterson fraudulently exhibited two yearling fillies which belonged to another farm, as his own, at the Iowa State Fair in 1907.

"We, the undersigned members of the firm of Finch Bros., hereby swear that at the Iowa State Fair, held in 1907, G.W. Patterson of the Patterson-Erickson Co., borrowed two yearling Percheron fillies from us, and exhibited them as his own.

Photo Courtesy of Philip Weber

These three Percherons were pulling this moving van in Columbus, Ohio, in 1906.

"The fillies in question were Gracieuse 51269 (71308) and Giosa 51268 (71264), and could not be shown by our firm because they had not been entered. G.W. Patterson borrowed them and exhibited them under the names of Sybil 46789 and Devilla 46787, and left his own fillies, which were entered under these names, in the barn.

"The animals were loaned to G.W. Patterson himself. We, the undersigned, were both in the ring when the fillies were shown and know that Mr. Patterson was present, and that the exhibition of the animals under false pretenses was done with his full knowledge and active participation in said exhibition. One of these fillies won second place.

"We, the undersigned members of the firm of Finch Bros., knew that this transaction was irregular and fraudulent, but on account

Photo Courtesy of Philip Weber

This barge scene photograph was taken in Pennsylvania sometime around the turn of the century and shows about ten Percheron work horses in service.

of the fact that said G.W. Patterson was superintendent of the Draft Horse show at the Minnesota State Fair, where we were to show the following week, did not feel disposed to refuse his request for temporary use of the fillies as his own."[24]

Following their investigation, Patterson was given notice to appear before the Board and "show cause why he should not be dealt with as our By-Laws provide."[25] Instead of appearing, Patterson sought an injunction to prevent the Society from taking any action on the case.

"The members of the Board of Directors and our members, may draw their own conclusion as to Mr. Patterson's reasons for charging Mr. McMillan and members of this Committee with fraud. Inasmuch as the other members of the Board may not realize how persistently and steadily the Pedigree Committee has worked, attention is respectfully called to the fact, that, during the last two years no less than twenty meetings of the Committee have been held, over 300 doubtful applications rejected and four extended field investigations made. As a result of our work one firm has been debarred from recording any American bred stock and restrictions laid upon its other business. Another firm detected in attempted irregularities, has been fined $200.00 and placed under strict restrictions on all future business, said restrictions requiring the firm in question to report all future colts before four months old (before they are weaned) and to pay the expenses of having same inspected at side of dam, by an authorized representative of the Society. Still another case, where the evidence indicated to the Committee that a certain party's statements were unworthy of credence, was handled in the same way. Every specific case on which charges have been filed, has been given proper attention.

"Not a single charge has been ever filed against any of the present members of the Board, and since the publication of these statements, Messrs. Patterson, Graham, Danforth and Carlson have all been called upon for specific charges, backed by proper evidence, by investigators employed by the Pedigree Committee, and all have refused, or been unable, to submit a single specific case.

"In conclusion your Pedigree Committee would respectfully call attention to the following facts:

"The present management of this Society has believed and still believes in the policy of building up, rather than tearing down. For

several years past, we have been providing additional rules governing the registration of animals with a view of placing every safeguard possible around the registration of animals and issuance of pedigrees.

"We now require that animals be recorded at a young age, we require transfers of mares, and in many other ways is every effort possible made to verify applications before pedigrees are issued.

"In accordance with the policy of the present management of the Society, we are making this report of the conditions that prevail and recommend putting same in print, in order that every stockholder may be fully informed concerning all matters in which he may be interested.

"This Society is composed of over four thousand stockholders, who are farmers and breeders throughout the United States and

Photo Courtesy of Philip Weber

At least 32 Percherons are pictured here in Nome, Alaska, where they worked for the W.J. Rowe Transfer Company in 1907.

Canada. The records of the Society belong to these stockholders, and they are the men who are interested in maintaining them. It is for that reason that your Committee has deemed it wise to place these facts so fully before the stockholders in order that they may have full opportunity to know the truth and act intelligently at the next Annual Meeting and future meetings that they attend."[26]

Patterson was by no means the only individual to attempt to discredit the association during its early years. The amount of money which could be made by the Percheron breed registry was enormous. The Percheron industry was gigantic and promised only to get larger. It is easy to forget that during that period, draft horses supplied Americans with their main source of motive power. And since the Percheron breed was more than three times as prevalent than any other draft horse breed, the persons who controlled the registry could reap large rewards. The association's business was big business, similar to something like General Motors today.

Membership Increases

Despite the difficulties encountered by the Society during this period, membership continued to increase significantly. In December, 1913, Society President A.P. Nave told the Society members attending the eleventh annual meeting that "our membership during the last year has increased from 4,831 members to 5,540, thus adding more than 700 new members to our already large membership."[27]

Some of the advantages to belonging to the Society were discussed in a piece in the Jan. 5, 1910, issue of the Breeder's Gazette where a reader's question is answered by Society President H.G. McMillan:

"I would like to know what advantage, if any, it would be to a farmer with a team of registered Percheron mares to belong to the Percheron Society of America. Does the Society pay any dividends or are the members liable for assessments under the rules and regulations?

"Every farmer owning a pair of registered Percheron mares should be a member of the Percheron Society of America. A share of stock costs only $10. The price for registration of American-bred animals to members is $2 and non-members $5; for imported animals, members $5, non-members $10, so that the cost of a

share of stock would soon be made up in the reduced price of registrations.

"In addition to the advantages of membership above stated every stock holder has a voice in the control and management of the association's affairs and is kept in constant touch with the breeding business through annual reports of the association and frequent letters and circulars sent out from the secretary's office.

"Furthermore, every farmer sufficiently interested in Percheron horses to own one or more pairs of pure-bred mares should lend his influence in helping along the breeding interests of the country to the extent at least of becoming a member of the Percheron Society of America and in that way actively identifying himself with the breeding interests."[28]

Within a few short years, the Percheron Society of America had established itself as a trustworthy livestock organization, had successfully defended that reputation, and began building up what would soon become the largest horse registry in the world.

References

[1]Breeder's Gazette, Jan. 19, 1910, p. 145.

[2]Breeder's Gazette, Feb. 16, 1910, p. 410.

[3]Minutes from the Seventh Annual Meeting of the Percheron Society of America held November 29, 1909.

[4]Ibid.

[5]Minutes from Eighth Annual Meeting, p. 8.

[6]Ibid.

[7]Ibid.

[8]Ibid, p. 11.

[9]Ibid.

[10]Ibid., p. 11.

[11]Ibid., p. 12.

[12]Ibid., pp. 12-13.

[13]Ibid., pp. 13-14.

[14]Ibid.

[15]Ibid., p. 15.

[16]Ibid., p. 17.

[17]Special Report of the Pedigree Committee to the Board of Directors of the Percheron Society of America regarding published charges concerning the Society., Oct. 3, 1911, Chicago, p. 1.

[18]Ibid., pp. 2-3.

[19]Ibid., p. 3.

[20]Ibid., p. 6.

[21]Ibid., p. 7.

[22]Ibid., pp. 7-8.

[23]Ibid., pp. 9-10.

[24]Ibid., p. 10-11.

[25]Ibid., p. 12.

[26]Ibid., pp. 13-14.

[27]Report of the 11th Annual Meeting of the Percheron Society of America, Dec. 1, 1913, Chicago, Ill.

[28]Breeder's Gazette, Jan. 5, 1910, p. 23.

The Glory Years

(1911-1931)

Dinsmore and other prominent Percheron horsemen promised an upbeat future for the American Percheron breeder. Others noted the declining influence of the imported horses in the show rings and bloodlines of the Percheron world. For the first time, American Percheron breeders were beginning to use homegrown stock in their breeding programs.

Ellis McFarland

Local Groups Organize

Ellis McFarland, who was later to become Society Secretary, wrote of the need for Percheron breeders to organize on local levels, as well as boost their national membership activity — an issue at the heart of all Society Secretaries to come later. McFarland wanted American breeders to quickly and effectively mobilize during the window of opportunity that opened when French breeding operations faltered.

"Percheron business is hindered more from the lack of proper local organization than from a sufficient number of adherents to the breed. There are many small breeders who are handicapped because few know what they have for sale. Buyers are reluctant to look them up if they have only one or two colts for sale. Here is where the country organization helps the unheard of breeder. Each member of the association chips in and that makes the advertising effective yet cheap for each one."[1]

Three early efforts at local Percheron organizations — two in Illinois and one in Ohio — had proven successful for at least some of their members during this time. The McLean County (Illinois) Percheron Association Secretary wrote that "although we have not been organized quite one year, we have done a great deal of good. We have published a sale list quarterly, and this has done much toward giving information as to where Percherons for sale are located."

Shortage of Draft Horses

The Secretary's report at the 1919 Annual Meeting of the Percheron Society of America included a brief discussion of what Dinsmore termed the "shortage of draft horses."

"Actual field surveys made by your secretary and assistant secretary this past season indicate that there are not one-third as many foals on farms as there should be to provide for the replacement needs of farmers in the corn belt. Those who have no foals or yearlings, and no mares bred to foal in 1920, are proceeding in the fond belief that someone else, somewhere else, is rearing enough young horses to take care of all needs two and three years hence. It is a fact that if two-thirds of the farmers in America who have been raising wheat quit producing same, it will only be a short time till there is not enough to go around, and the same thing is true of horses, though more time must elapse before the scarcity is felt. Some are holding off in the belief that other types of motive power will replace draft horses wholly or in large part. Argument is wasted on such individuals, but they will eventually pay dearly for their experience, as thousands of others have already done."[2]

Tractor, Truck Threat Dismissed

As the business of raising horses returned to normal in the U.S., the question of the gasoline-powered tractor's influence on agriculture and, consequently, on horse breeding again dominated discussions. The 1920 Percheron Review included a foreword which stated that tractors and trucks "are no more destined to remove the draft horse from the realm of agricultural production than was the locomotive."

Secretary Wayne Dinsmore

Society President E.B. White, at the Society's annual meeting Dec. 1, 1919, gave a lengthy opening speech dealing squarely with the topic. After explaining the link between horse breeding and the agriculture economy, White dismissed the up and coming tractor power as posing no threat to horse-powered farming. A gasoline-based system will be too expensive to operate, White argued.

"The less grain there is fed on the farm, the more there is to go on the market; and consequently, the lower the price will fall. The more gas engines, trucks, tractors, and so forth, the farmer buys, the greater will be the consumption of gas and the higher the price. Gentlemen, is this working in the interest of the farmer, or in the interest of the oil magnates or tractor and truck manufacturers? You all know that the most successful farmers in your neighborhood are the ones who come nearest to producing what they need. They buy the least, and this will always be true. The farmer who produces his own motive power for working his farm will always have more money in the bank and be more independent than the one who buys his power units and the fuel to operate them. Horse power is the cheapest farm power."[3]

In the Sept. 9, 1920 Breeder's Gazette, Professor A.B. Caine of Iowa State College stated that horses are still preferred for farm power by many farmers.

"The demand for draft horses of good breeding is increasing with amazing rapidity. We have received many requests at the college from farmers in all parts of this country and Canada for draft horses and have been forced to turn down the majority of them on account of an inadequate supply of good stock. The American-bred horse has found great favor with the large farmers of the Canada and the northwest. The type of Belgian bred in the United States seems to be the most popular horse among Canadians, but they do not discriminate against breed or color and are willing to take almost anything of a draft type with good breeding. A horse does not need to be a purebred, but it must have the ability to do a full day's work.

President E.B. White

"The tractor craze is gradually wearing off, and farmers are rapidly coming back to horses. Last spring it was not an uncommon sight on the great farms of Canada and the western part of the United States to see tractors standing idle and dismantled in one corner of a field, while horses were working day in and day out.

"Good horses are bringing prices unheard of a few years back. Not long ago Dean C.F. Curtiss sold a young Percheron filly for $3,000, a price which is thought to be a world's record. Horsemen all over the country are sending in reports that demand by far exceeds the present supply and are appealing to farmers to breed more draft horses of the utility type. Small, chunky horses have lived their day but big, rugged work horses, which possess refinement combined with the ability to work a number of years, are wanted.

"We are facing an acute shortage of suitable brood mares, as well as stallions, thereby making the problem of increasing production more perplexing than the average person realizes. Farmers and breeders cannot look to European countries for aid for various reasons. First of all they are busy increasing their own production. Moreover, they are not in sympathy with the methods and practices of our breeders. They feel that their method of breeding and their type of horses are the best. Nevertheless, it is the American type of

Photo Courtesy of Cook & Gormley

A team of large, upstanding Percheron mares hooked to a spiked-tooth harrow.

horse that is in greatest demand at present. It is to be hoped that farmers will answer the call for more and better horses."[4]

The perceived threat to the horse industry's future from tractor and truck power prompted many horsemen to significantly reduce their herds, despite assurances from draft horse industry leaders of the day.

"Wherever tractors have been tried to the exclusion of horses, failure has resulted. Neither in the United States or Canada, on large farms or small ones, can satisfactory operations be carried on without the horse. Unlike Othello, the Venetian Moor of Shakespeare's fancy, whose occupation ceased, old Dobbin is still going strong and is likely to continue so. He is more reliable than any mechanical contrivance ever invented, and is in better standing today than he was fifty years ago, which proves the country's appreciation of its merits and indispensability."[5]

As the years went on, more draft horse breeders and others economically tied to the horse-drawn industry wrote of the advantages of horse power over tractors and trucks in the leading agricultural journals. But at the same time, advertisements for tractors, trucks and other agricultural machines began edging out the horses in the same publications.

Horse Association of America

Wirth Dunham of the Wayne, Ill., Oaklawn Farm spoke of the newly-founded Horse Association of America during the 20th Annual Meeting of the Percheron Society of America Dec. 4, 1922, at the Union Stock Yards in Chicago.

The Association, Dunham explained, was to promote the interests of all persons involved in the horse industry and who were, consequently, threatened by the arrival of gasoline and electric power. This large group included saddlery and harness makers, light and heavy horse breeders, and horseshoe manufacturers, among others.

By soliciting funds from the interested parties — the light horse businesses and corresponding cottage industries provided the most capital — the association proposed making an intensive effort to promote horses (both light and draft, as well as mules) to power business and industry.

"We will say there are 12,000 retail coal dealers in the United States. We prepare a pamphlet that deals exclusively with retail

Horses-Mules Power-Profit

HORSE and MULE ASSOCIATION of AMERICA
(Formerly Horse Association of America)
CHICAGO, ILL.

The Horse and Mule Association of America, formerly the Horse Association of America, published this bulletin in 1928. After leaving the Percheron Society of America, Wayne Dinsmore became an active Secretary for this group which is now the Draft Horse and Mule Association of America.

coal dealers with information that has been collected not only from one city but from a number of cities, and send it out to the retail coal dealers. Maybe the first pamphlet does not receive any attention, but the second may reach him at a time when he has not been making very much money. This pamphlet tells him how he can save some money and it receives considerable attention. He pays more attention to the third pamphlet and as he becomes more interested and looks into his costs, our battle is won, for he begins to buy horses."[7]

The Horse Association of America later took mules into its ranks to become the Horse and Mule Association of America. The organization continued to espouse the advantages of using horses over tractors and trucks through the 1920s and '30s and also helped to educate the teamster on how to best use his horses and mules in farming.

The Percheron breeders which found lively trade were those raising large, athletic horses, both for show as well as work. And

Photo Courtesy of Philip Weber

This ice and coal delivery wagon was in service in Cleveland, Ohio, in 1926.

the trend toward the large horses was likely to continue, said Secretary McFarland during the 21st Annual Meeting in December 1923.

White Resigns, Butler Elected

It was at the same meeting that then Association President E.B. White tendered his resignation. White, who was succeeded by W.H. Butler, had served as president for thirteen years. He died three years later. White was later honored as the first to be named to the Percheron Association's Hall of Fame in December, 1935.

Larger Horses

Those who still used wagons to transport goods were using larger vehicles and so required large horses, McFarland said. On the Chicago market, 1,300 to 1,400 pound horses sold for about $100 per head "whereas good draft geldings weighing 1,900 pounds to a ton are bringing $300 and over," he said.

President W.H. Butler

Photo Courtesy of Philip Weber

A number of Percherons stand ready to begin their city deliveries.

"As Secretary of your Society, I feel that I should call your attention to the importance of the matter of type. As nearly as I can tell from talking with market men, breeders of Percherons and dealers, there is a very decided trend among farmers to favor the thick-made, deep-ribbed, heavy-boned type of Percheron. Our ultimate aim in breeding Percheron horses is to produce the kind of stallions that will sire the best market geldings."[8]

Bigger Hitches

In addition to using larger horses, farmers were also encouraged to use bigger hitches for their farm work. In the 1927 Percheron Review, Secretary McFarland wrote "How to Make More Money by Working More Horses per Team." At the top of the article is a photograph of a farmer driving eighteen horses hitched to a double-disc. The horses are hitched four abreast, four deep, with two abreast in the front.

"I know a farmer who is getting into debt deeper each year. He has wasted several thousand dollars on machinery. His barn lot is half full of old machinery not in use any more. He tries to use a

Ellis McFarland ran this photograph in the 1928 Percheron Review. The caption reads: "The above photo shows 18 Percherons hitched so as to work with perfect ease. They are driven by a single pair of lines extending to the lead pair only. Such a team can pull three double discs and cover 60 acres per day. Teams of this size are particularly suited to work on farms where fields are 80 acres or up in size."

tractor for everything. His horses look like the kind that are usually found hauling a Gypsy wagon through the country. When he does work them in the field, he hitches four of these small weak horses abreast to a gang plow or the same number to a small harrow. He uses a single row cultivator to plow his corn. His mechanical turn of mind is responsible for his old dilapidated looking buildings because he cannot get enough money ahead to ever do any painting or repairing. This farm was left to him by his father. Poor man! Too bad! I feel sorry for him. He is typical, however, of a certain class of farmers who have grown to considerable proportions in recent years.

"Across the road from where this man lives is a different type of a farmer. He, too, represents a distinct class but there are not nearly so many that go in his group as in the case of the other farmer. This man has grown wealthy farming. What little machinery he has is kept in the shed when it is not in use. I do not believe that he has a horse on his farm which will weigh under 1,600 lbs. He sold two pairs of geldings the other day for $1,250. He raised them and they had done his farm work. One rarely ever sees this man going to the field to put in a crop driving less than eight horses and sometimes ten. He caught on to this new idea of using larger team units very quickly. A tractor never did appeal to him. He has always worked good big teams. His buildings and fences are all painted and in first class shape. He has a moderate priced automobile. His children are being educated. In fact, everything about his farm indicates that the owner is in a thrifty condition financially.[9]

McFarland encouraged farmers interested in hooking larger hitches, but unsure of their abilities to do so, to contact Horse Association of America Secretary Wayne Dinsmore — formerly the secretary of the Percheron Society — to receive a complete set of diagrams for hooking large, multiple hitches. The Horse Association was not the first to suggest the larger hitches. E.A. White of the University of Illinois advocated larger hitches almost ten years earlier, but McFarland and others linked the need for larger hitches directly to an answer to the tractor question.

"There is another reason why farmers should work more horses besides the fact that they can do much more work at less cost. When they work horses they provide a market for the hay and grain which they produce. When farmers use mechanical power they must purchase fuel from an industry which is in no way

connected to agriculture. This is another way of saying that when a man farms with a tractor he is destroying a big market for the crop which he produces on his own farm. Gilbert Gusler, a Chicago economist, says that '20 percent of our corn crop is consumed by horses and mules, ranking next to hogs which consume 40 percent.'

"There is a vast difference between paying out actual cash every time you fill your tractor engine with gas and oil and getting the same amount of energy from horses which feed much of the time from a crop that cannot be marketed. In the one case the farmer is marketing what he would like to sell instead of paying out hard-earned money to get power to do his work."[10]

Breed Style Changes

While Percheron Society officials encouraged farmers to use larger horses and more of them, the Percheron breed itself was indeed changing, but not in such a way as to meet their recommendations. Clark Wolfington, who worked for such notable Percheron breeders as Wirth Dunham of Oaklawn Farm, W.S. Corsa of Gregory Farm and the Tom Corwin Farms, wrote of his thirty years of experience with Percherons in the 1927 Review.

"Twenty to thirty years ago the kind of a Percheron stallion that found greatest favor among good judges was the heavy boned, short backed, deep ribbed, thick set horse. After that time there seemed to develop a craze for stylish, upstanding Percherons. So today we find altogether too many Percheron stallions through the country that are too light in bone and lack in depth and thickness of body. Many of our breeders went too far in trying to develop quality. We grooms know the difficulties encountered in trying to put the fat on the slim-waisted kind in order to make them look like drafters. If we have to make a long ship, the fat melts away, the middle shrinks up and we haven't much horse left.

"During the time mentioned, the breeders who kept in mind as an ideal this deep-bodied, heavy-boned type of a Percheron but who developed quality along with size have succeeded best.

"Now many of our breeders are beginning to see that they must go back part way to the type of a Percheron we liked twenty years ago. Farmers are demanding the change as well as city users. Of course, the man who kept the size and substance in his

Percherons along with quality has the type that finds greatest favor among our best judges today."[11]

References

[1]Ellis McFarland, "Percheron Breeders Should Organize," The Percheron Review, (1916), p. 24.

[2]Percheron Review, (1920), Minutes of Annual Meeting of Percheron Society of America, Dec. 1, 1919.

[3]"Report of the 17th Annual Meeting of the Percheron Society of America," The Percheron Review, (1920), p. 3.

[4]Breeder's Gazette, "The Demand for Horses", Sept. 9, 1920, p. 481.

[5]Review, 1928, p. 5.

[6]Report of the 20th Annual Meeting of the Percheron Society of America," The Percheron Review, (1923), p. 14.

[7]Report of the 21st Annual Meeting of the Percheron Society of America," The Percheron Review, (1924), p. 11.

[8]Percheron Review, "How to Make More Money by Working More Horses Per Team", 1927, p. 6.

[9]Percheron Review, "Multiple Horse Hitches," 1919, p. 3.

[10]Percheron Review, 1927, p. 9.

[11]Ibid., p. 11.

The End of an Era

(1931-1948)

Despite the best efforts of McFarland and other Percheron Society officers and of Percheron breeders, interest in the Percheron — and draft horses in general — began falling off in the late 1920s and early 30s. As an example, the Percheron Review, which had published 60 to 70 pages of Percheron news in the early 1920s, began publishing smaller, 15 to 20 page magazines in the early 1930s which contained little more than show results and some advertisements.

Chicago Union Stockyards Fire

The Society was dealt a major setback in May, 1934, with a disastrous fire at the Chicago Union Stockyards.

Photo Courtesy of Percheron Horse Associaiton

The Union Stockyards fire consumed the offices of Percheron Horse Association of America.

The first five months of 1934 were extremely dry in Chicago as only 3.91 inches of rain fell between Jan. 1 and May 19. On May 19, 1934 a great fire overwhelmed the Union Stock Yards, destroying a great number of livestock pens, runways, barns, and other buildings as well as more than 800 head of livestock.[1] Also destroyed in the fire were the offices of various breed associations, including those of the Percheron Society of America.

"On May 19, 1934, shortly before 4:21 p.m., a fire started in the cattle pens of the Union Stock Yard and Transit Company's property in the vicinity of 43rd and Morgan streets. The fire was discovered by company watchmen, patrolling this district, who immediately sent in the alarm from an A.D.T. fire alarm box, located in a watchman's shanty at 43rd and Morgan streets.

"The fire was in all probability caused by a cigarette discarded from an automobile passing over the frame 43rd

Before the fire, the Percheron Horse Association used this office for most of its business. Note the large number of file cabinets along the walls.

In this "after the fire" photo, the file cabinets can be seen on the right, completely destroyed, and a number of safes which appear to have survived.

Photos Courtesy of Cook & Gormley

street viaduct. This ignited loose hay in the pens and, fanned by a moderate southwest wind, the flames spread rapidly in all directions, but principally northeast. Ready fuel was furnished by the wooden framework of the pens, made extremely flammable by the prevailing drought conditions, by the elevated frame cattle runways with hay storage sheds above, and by the frame viaducts."[2]

In the end, about $6 million of property was lost in the fire, which consumed almost two-thirds of the stock yards. At least one man was killed in the blaze as he tried to herd sheep from a burning building. But while the Percheron Society of America was forced to move its offices to the Boys' and Girls' Club Building in the Union Stock Yards after the fire, the Percheron Association

Photo Courtesy of Cook & Gormley

Following the fire, all of the records of association business, including certificates of registration were laid out to dry.

did not lose all of its valuable records of registrations "because of the foresight of the man (Ellis McFarland) who had been guiding its affairs through the years in obtaining fireproof safes for the records of the breed." In fact, the association's business of handling registrations and transfers "went on within forty-eight hours after the fire had broken out."[3]

Percheron Business Improves

With the exception of the fire, 1934 was a good year for the Percheron industry and 1935 promised to be even brighter, according to McFarland in the 1935 Percheron Review:

"The 'old grey mare' is fast becoming what she used to be judging by the demand for mares coming into the Percheron Association office at Chicago.

"On the January 15th buyers' list there were 232 names; by February 15, 242 more buyers had written in wanting to get Percherons, and by March 12, another 165 had requested to buy, a total of 639 buyers since December 1, 439 of whom wanted mares."[4]

After several years of tapering off, membership in the Percheron Society once again began to climb.

"After the Armistice the draft horse business suffered a decline. Our surplus food was no longer needed in Europe and the wheels of the reaper were stilled. The tractor and the truck crept gradually into use in the city and on the large farm. Percheron registrations, always in harmony with agriculture, reached their low point in 1932.

"Then came an anti-climax. The tractor, like much of the other installment-bought equipment of the inflation period, was bankrupting its owner. A 'horse motor' could be produced on the farm at little cost, whereas a tractor cost a farmer into three figures to start on, into two figures for annual interest. A tractor took cold hard cash to fuel but a draft horse fueled himself right on the place. He also returned the good elements in that fuel to the soil as fertilizer. Best of all, the draft horse made possible a return to diversified farming at a time when specialized farming had failed. Sensible men saw in the draft horse the only sure cure for America's agriculture gone down into debt and tenantry."[5]

In 1932, only 1,892 horses were registered with the Society. In 1934, 3,224 horses were registered. The two following years were even better as 4,836 horses were registered in 1935 and 5,028 were given papers in 1936 — the most horses registered in a single year since 1923. The bloom was not to last long, however, as registrations fell off again slowly up to and through World War II — after which the numbers then plummeted.

Society Changes Name

In 1934 the Society was changed from a corporation organized for profit to one with a nonprofit status. The name was also changed from the Percheron Society of America to the Percheron Horse Association of America — the name the Association still uses today.[6]

The resurgence in Percheron business in the early 1930s fueled a renewal in Association publicity and other activities as

Most of the horses pulling milk wagons were white or dapple gray Percherons. In this case, Supplee's Dairy used a black Percheron.

the Association came into more money from registrations and registry transfers. The Association altered its annual Percheron Review in 1935 to a smaller format and began printing more show reports and other Association publications.

"The Percheron Review which was issued in 1935 brought such an enthusiastic response it was necessary to have 3,000 additional copies printed. About 7,000 copies of the Review were sent out during the year; whereas, not more than 2,500 copies were sent out in previous years. It will be necessary to print at least 10,000 copies of the 1936 Review."[7]

The Percheron News was altered in 1939 from a newspaper format to a quarterly magazine. The January 1939 issue carried a full page advertisement by the Association promoting Percherons:

"Men and women who live on the land are coming to understand one thing well — that it takes a diversified livestock program to put farming on a profitable basis and keep it there.

"Prosperity becomes not a pleasant daydream but a solid reality to the farmer who fits into his program the faithful broodmare that works in the collar and raises a colt every year; the milk cow with a good calf; the brood sow with her two annual litters of pigs, and the ewe that throws twin lambs frequently. Drouths, wars, high taxes, unsteady markets for farm products, misfortunes of every kind, come and go, but of this the farmer may be sure: The dependable mothers of the farmyard go right on reproducing themselves and thereby putting dollars in the bank."[8]

The Breed Type Studies

In 1934, the Association, in an attempt to better unify Percheron breeders and judges in terms of the ideal Percheron type, launched a program of breed type studies and conferences to determine the ideal Percheron type. Because the fire of 1934 destroyed many of the reports made out by a number of breeders concerning the study, the program was launched again in 1936.

"Pictures of 25 outstanding stallions and 25 outstanding mares, all but three or four of which were grand champions at the International Live Stock Exposition at Chicago, were sent out with a questionnaire to 100 of our most prominent breeders, grooms, judges and agricultural college instructors. The International winners were chosen because through the years that show has been

considered the court of highest appeal. Then, too, this was the only show of which pictures were available for all the winners during the past 20 years. The group represented the tops for each year in so far as they were available."[9]

In the first study, Calypso 25017 was judged as the ideal type of a Percheron stallion. Calypso was foaled in May, 1897. He was purchased and imported by the firm of Dunham, Fletcher and Coleman of the Oaklawn Farm, Wayne, Ill., and exhibited by that firm at the 1900 International Live Stock Exposition in Chicago where he was named reserve grand champion. One of the three judges at the International was H.G. McMillan — who later became President of the Percheron Society. McMillan was so impressed by the three-year-old Calypso that he persuaded

Calypso 25017 was judged as the ideal type of a Percheron stallion in 1934.

Dunham, Fletcher and Coleman to sell him. McMillan brought Calypso back with him to his Lakewood Farm in Rock Rapids, Iowa, where he spent most of the rest of his life.

Calpyso was given a rating of 2,058 out of a possible 2,500. Dragon 52155 finished second with 2,014 points, Sir Laet 190277 was third with 1,930 points, Jerome 160754 was fourth with 1,852, and Laet 133886 came in fifth with a rating of 1,817.

Carnona V 158285 was named the ideal type of a Percheron mare during the first type study. Foaled in June 21, 1919, Carnona was bred by W.S. Corsa of White Hall, Ill., and sired by Corsa's famous stallion Carnot 66666. The mare was shown to success by Maryvale Farms of Youngstown, Ohio, and later owned by W.H. Butler of Columbus, Ohio.

Carnona V received a rating of 2,033, followed by Brigue 202512 with 1,741 points, LaBelle 34982 with 1,671, Laet's

Carnona V, a daughter of Carnot, was named ideal type Percheron mare in 1934. She was bred by W.S. Corsa.

Magic Queen 190170 with 1,670, and Maplegrove Leila 156680 with 1,653.

In 1937 the second breed type study was handled differently and was called the All American Best Ten Stallions and Mares. Twelve judges at the largest shows in the Midwest in 1936 and 1937 were asked to select the ten best stallions and mares from a collection of 91 pictures (46 mares and 45 stallions). These horses were all grand champions at all major shows during 1936 and 1937. None were included from the first breed type study save for three: Sir William, Damascus and Maple Leaf Crescent.[10]

In this study, Enchanter 212346 owned by Pine Tree Farms, McHenry, Ill., was named the most ideal type of a Percheron Stallion with 119 points out of a possible 120. In mares, Lancinante 225458 owned by Conner's Prairie Farm, Noblesville, Ind., was named the ideal mare type with 100 points out of 120.

The third breed type study was conducted in 1938 and gave the prizes to the same two winners as in the previous year, implying that judges were somewhat uniform in their opinions. The breed type conferences held from 1934 to 1939 were very successful as breeders, judges and grooms discussed with one another the merits of individual horses and the importance of certain characteristics in determining an animal's worth.

In 1939, the fourth breed type study was conducted — again differently from past contests. This time, in addition to having the judges from the most important shows judge the animals, breeders were encouraged to make their selections from a group of photographs published in the January, 1940, Percheron News (30 stallions, 35 mares).[11]

In that contest, Nesus 231550, an imported four-year-old owned by Robert W. Lyons of Lewisville, Ind., was named first place stallion. In the mares, Julie, 234076, an imported gray six year old owned by Robert W. Lyons, Lewisville, Ind., was made first place mare.

Registrations Drop

In the last years of the '30s and first years of the '40s, Percheron registrations began to sink. In 1937, 4,611 horses were registered. In 1945, only 845 horses were entered into the official register. And nine years later, the number had fallen away to a mere 85 animals registered. The most significant reason for the decline of the Percheron — and all other breeds of draft horses in the U.S. — was the victory of tractor power over horse power. Despite the arguments of Association officials, Percheron breeders and others, American farmers used horses less and less on their farms.

The end was delayed throughout the early 1940s because of first, the Great Depression, and second, World War II.

Enchanter (left) and Lancinante were named ideal type stallion and mare in 1937.

Nesus (left) and Julie won the ideal type stallion and mare awards in 1939.

Depression, War Prolong Draft Horse Use

The Great Depression of the 1930s gave credence to the argument set forth by Ellis McFarland and others that draft horse power can allow a farmer to maintain profits by limiting the amount of goods he buys. Because horses are fueled by home-grown commodities such as grain and hay, horse farmers can continue to operate longer during harsh economic times than their motorized counterparts who must use cash for their fuel. The argument was sound for the day.

Shortly after the economy had improved in the late 1930s, the draft horse industry was granted another reprieve, this time in the form of World War II. While the war also tended to reduce the amount of feed available for work horses, the wartime demand for machinery and fuel to power the war effort left fewer machines and gasoline to be bought by the American farmer as well. In fact, using horses on the farm was something of a patriotic mission. With the men gone to fight the Axis powers, women were left at home in charge of working the horses as evident in the following article published in the July, 1944 Percheron News:

Andrew Hoover of Springfield, Mo., saved his money while overseas in the wartime service by sending it home. And when his father was hurt in a tractor-rollover, Andrew returned home to take over the farm. The first thing he did was buy a team of Percherons, according to the July, 1944, Percheron News.

"Girls are handling husky ton Percherons with the greatest of ease. This job, like so many oth-

ers in machine shops and factories, has always been considered men's work; but, in the past few years, we have become accustomed to seeing women taking over many man-sized jobs.

"Although the Percherons sense the inexperienced hands at the reins, they obey every command. The gentleness of the Percherons was pointed out by G.T. Burrows writing from England: 'The members of the Woman's Land Army working among horses have proved satisfactory, especially with Percherons whose docility makes them easy to handle and well suited to female labor.'"[12]

As the end of the draft horse era approached, McFarland continued to promote the Percheron horse and horse farming in general.

"Those of us who are older and have weathered many of these periods have learned they are but passing phases, that the cycle in which we are now caught will again swing upward and restore better days and therefore, we know how unwise it can be to act too hastily, to become unduly alarmed by prevailing conditions. We

Mary Garen of Mt. Sterling, Ohio, drove this Percheron team during the summer of 1944.

know that stock disposed of at low prices will need to be replaced at not too distant a future and at much higher prices. Let us consider all of this carefully with an eye to our future and to community needs before we act. And it is at this point that we who are more experienced must ask those to try to develop foresight."[13]

Ellis McFarland Dies

Ellis McFarland, Secretary-Treasurer of the Percheron Horse Association for 28 years, died unexpectedly Oct. 26, 1948, at the age of 59. McFarland had been active in the Percheron industry for most of his life, serving as assistant secretary to then Secretary Wayne Dinsmore from 1914 until Dinsmore's retirement in 1920. Upon becoming assistant secretary, McFarland's first task was to interview various Percheron breeders to help

The January, 1943, Percheron Review ran the above cartoon drawn by the son of a Percheron farmer. The cartoon is typical of the tone of the Percheron News during Ellis McFarland's tenure as the association's secretary. In addition to meeting minutes, breeder's advertisements and show results, McFarland stuffed the publication with numerous stories about farmers who first fail with tractors and later succeed with horses.

research the Percheron's history for the book *A History of the Percheron Horse* by Alvin Sanders and Wayne Dinsmore. Sanders, of course, was the son of James H. Sanders, founder of the first Percheron Stud Book, and served as editor of "The Breeder's Gazette" and "The Livestock Journal."

"It was my pleasure and privilege to undertake some twenty years ago, in collaboration with my good friend Wayne Dinsmore — then Secretary of the Percheron Society of America — the preparation of the story of the origin and the introduction into this country of the Percheron horse. It so happened that, at that time, a

Ellis McFarland died Oct. 26, 1948, after 28 years of service to the Association.

young man by the name of Ellis McFarland entered service in the Percheron office."[14]

McFarland was raised on a farm, the son of a horse breeder.

"He was reared on a 250-acre farm in Adams County, near Quincy, Ill., Mr. McFarland early manifested a deep interest in horses. His father was an admirer of good horseflesh and kept draft stallions, trotting and coach horses, jacks and jennets. At the age of 21 years Mr. McFarland left the farm to take up his studies at the University of Illinois. How well he applied himself to his work there is attested to by the fact that in 1913 he won the state judging contest, receiving a medal awarded by the Illinois Live Stock Breeders Association to the best judge of horses.

"It is interesting to note that he has continued his studies at night school, specializing in finance and business law to better fit him for assisting the Finance Committee of the Association in managing the invested funds of the association, and for handling its legal problems. In 1928, when the Percheron News was started, he began taking courses in advertising and journalism in order to edit a better draft horse paper and meet the needs of Percheron breeders."[15]

Association Secretary Anne Brown

Following his death, a memorial service was held at the association's office, Nov. 29, 1948. Peter Templeton of Evansville, Wis., a close friend of McFarland and his family, read a memorial service:

"It is usually when we least expect it and when we are least prepared for it, that we are called upon to part with someone upon whose leadership and friendship we have come to depend. It is so in the case of Ellis McFarland or 'Mac' as many of us affectionately called him.

"The heritage he left us will outlast gold and fame. It is not easy to hold fast to ideals and to live by them in the world of battle where each man is struggling to succeed.

"'Mac's' battle was never easy. Yet he held fast to the truth, honesty and integrity. He never surrendered the fight for these. And we who are left to evaluate what he did for us — are deeply grateful to him. We are also deeply grateful, that although

he left us, the light is not extinguished, but shines on, a beacon to guide we of his generation and of his interests."[16]

Anne Brown Made Secretary

Following McFarland's death, Anne Brown was made secretary-treasurer of the association. Brown had served as secretary to McFarland for 20 years prior to his death in 1948 and had worked in the association offices since 1914.

When Anne Brown retired in 1965 as Secretary, she had been a faithful employee of the association for more than half a century and wrote the following article in the Spring, 1965 Percheron Notes:

"It is expected that before the publication of another issue of Percheron Notes, I shall have retired as Secretary-Treasurer of the Association. I first entered the employ of the Percheron Society of America on Oct. 14, 1914, when Mr. Wayne Dinsmore was Secretary. In those years all drayage was done by draft horses. The Fire Department next to our office on Exchange Ave., Union Stock Yards, Chicago, and which office we lost in the disastrous Stock Yards Fire of May 1934, always had a team of grey Percherons. All the packers and all the breweries used draft horses as well as all other business concerns. Business at the Percheron office was brisk in those days with an office force of twenty or more girls, some of whom I still number among my best friends.

"After an absence of some years, I returned to the office in 1928. Following World War I business declined until 1933, the office force was down to four girls. The pickup in the draft horse business during the depression due to the low prices for grain necessitated an increase in the office force. Prior to World War II with a step-up in publicity plus an increase in registrations and transfers, the office force again increased to around twenty girls. However, following World War II, a steady decline was experienced so that at the time of the death of Mr. Ellis McFarland in October of 1948, we were down to three employees."[17]

Brown took over the offices of the Percheron Association during what many consider was its most critical period. The Percheron horse was beginning to disappear from the American farm landscape. And, despite efforts a few years earlier by McFarland and others to stimulate markets overseas and in South America, the demand for Percherons continued to decline rapidly.

References

[1]Report of Union Stock Yard And Transit Company Conflagration, Chicago, Ill., May 19, 1934, prepared by The Chicago Board of Underwriters of Chicago., p. 2.

[2]Ibid., p. 4.

[3]Percheron News, July, 1939, pp. 30-31.

[4]Percheron Review, 1935, p. 5.

[5]Percheron News, July, 1939, pp. 8-9.

[6]Ibid., p. 6.

[7]Secretary's Report at the Annual Meeting of the Percheron Horse Association of America, Dec. 2, 1935.

[8]Percheron News, January, 1939, p. 79.

[9]Percheron Review, January, 1936.

[10]Percheron Premium List, 1938, p. 26.

[11]Percheron News, January, 1940.

[12]Percheron News, July, 1944.

[13]Percheron News, January, 1945.

[14]Alvin H. Sanders, Percheron News, July, 1939, p. 11.

[15]Ibid., p. 30.

[16]Percheron News, January, 1949, p. 7.

[17]Percheron Notes, Spring, 1965, p. 4.

Hard Times

(1949-1981)

The 1949 U.S. census indicated that there were 5,921,000 head of horses in the U.S. — a decrease of 10 percent over the past year and the smallest of any year on record. The best year on record for horses in the U.S. was 1915 when the census found 21,431,000 horses in America. Numbers declined gradually until 1943, when they began to fall much more quickly.[1]

Lack of Replacement Stock

What was perhaps more alarming, however, was that in 1949 there were fewer than 400,000 horses under two years of age in the U.S. Without young horses to serve as replacements, the horse population was sure to sink further. Hopes began to wane among even the staunchest draft horse supporters.

As evidenced by this photograph of a halter class at the 1948 Indiana State Fair, some interest in the draft horse remained into the late 1940s.

The straw to break the camel's back perhaps came when agricultural colleges throughout the country began dropping draft horses from their studies. In 1950, Secretary Anne Brown wrote the following editorial on the subject:

"Disregarding the fact draft horse breeders of any state are also taxpayers, and therefore, should have a word to say about the matter, there are still other factors to consider. Chiefly, it is believed that draft horses should be available to the agricultural student, that he may have the opportunity to understand their potentialities as a supplementary power unit even on today's highly mechanized farms, particularly, since as yet, no one has control over the weather, and drafters have proved conclusively, in all parts of the country, that from this standpoint alone, if not from any other, they are a necessary adjunct to a well-planned farm program."[2]

Despite the many signs of the decline of the draft horse in America, writers continued to emphasize the importance of "keeping at least one team on every farm." Many of these articles appeared in the Percheron publications.

"None of this group (draft horse supporters) would try to convince any farmer today, that the use of horse-power exclusively, is the

The aged mare class at the 1949 National Percheron Show.

only way to farm, although many farmers in many localities find it the best way for them. (This is because of the fact that the investment is next to nothing as compared to a fully motorized farm.) But they do believe, that on a one-man-farm, or a two-man-farm there is no better or more economical combination than to use a tractor for the heavy work, such as plowing, discing, cultivating, corn grinding and other belt power, and to use a team of horses for the light work. This makes it unnecessary to buy the second tractor and all tractor machinery to go with it."[3]

Despite all the arguments, rationalizations and pleas, the draft horse fell from favor. And were it not for the few American families which continued to raise Percherons, the breed would have likely been driven to near extinction in the U.S. before the resurgence in interest in draft horses came about in the late 1970s and '80s.

Association Faces Financial Hardship

Percheron business fell off so dramatically, in fact, that the Association faced severe financial hardship in the mid 1950s. In 1984, former Association President Ray Bast wrote a brief history of the association during the past 40 years:

"About forty years ago the Percheron Horse Association of America had its offices in an upstairs building on Halstead Street in the City of Chicago, next to Chicago International Amphitheater. This was a large office, larger than necessary at the time. As the Percheron business became smaller and the work became less, the members and its officers did not cut back and more money was spent than income. It was about that time the association had about $70,000 in the treasury. In less than ten years the assets had dwindled and there was not enough money to carry on."[4]

George A. Dix, who was elected President of the Association in the Fall of 1952, wrote an open letter to all members of the association which was published in the Spring, 1954, issue of the Percheron Notes:

"At the annual meeting held December 3, 1953, the Secretary reported that we had a deficit of over $4,000 during the 1953 fiscal year, and that with the contem-

Society President Ray Bast and wife Helen. Ray served as president of the society from 1965 to 1984.

plated loss of the outside typing work which has been done in our office for the past several years for the beef cattle associations, and the decline in our business, we might expect an average deficit of around $6,000 a year. As everything possible has been done to reduce expenses and still maintain the present office, it was apparent that something must be done. The Secretary also reported that for personal reasons, it would be necessary for her to move this spring from Chicago to a farm which she and her husband own in northwestern Indiana.

"Several suggestions were made as to the future of the Association, among which was the possibility of combining our office with the office of the Belgian Draft Horse Association of Wabash, Indiana, or building a small concrete block building on the farm owned by Mrs. Brown and entering into a contract with her to maintain the records there."[5]

Association Moved to Brown Home

Ultimately, the association decided upon the latter arrangement. A two-car garage was built on the Brown property for about $2,000. After about seven years, the building became the property of Brown who then rented it to the association for $400 per year.

The association sold of much of its property, including desks, typewriters, chairs and other office equipment, but kept the large safes to hold the association files. At this time, the Percheron Association temporarily suspended its publishing activities. A few years later, they were able to come out with a new publication, The Percheron Notes, to replace the Percheron News. The first publications were small, four

The Bast Family included (back row) Brothers Ray, Art and Roland and (front row) Mr. and Mrs. Val Bast. Ray and Art, at their own individual farms, were among the few Percheron breeders who stuck it out through the hard times of the 1950s and 60s, and continued to raise quality Percherons.

page affairs, but helped to maintain an avenue of communication between the association and its members and between members themselves. Anne Brown wrote the following notice in the first Percheron Notes:

"Following the discontinuance of the Percheron News magazine which was published by the Association for twelve years, our breeders felt the need for some kind of a medium in which to advertise the horses they have for sale and to keep them posted on the news of the business of the Association.

"The Board of Directors voted to publish a small newspaper, provided the money to cover the cost of the printing and postage could be obtained through advertising space sold.

"The Secretary is very gratified at the cooperation received from the breeders on this first issue of the paper. It is hoped that with such a good start, this paper may be continued on a 'pay as you go' basis."[6]

Worst Years for Breed, Association

At about this time, the Percheron breed endured its worst years. More than 3,500 Percherons were registered during 1939, yet ten years later, only 253 Percherons were given papers during 1949. The decline was rapid and dramatic. From 1950 to 1970, only 3,091 Percheron horses were registered. After 1970, the numbers increased gradually until the early 1980s when they began rising more quickly. More than 1,000 horses were registered each year from 1982 until 1990, the time of this writing.[7]

Another indicator of just how bleak things had become was found in the showring. The number of exhibitors at the major shows — numbering in the thousands in earlier years — had dwindled to less than a hundred during the years in the mid 1950s and 60s. In 1956, a total of only 30 Percheron exhibitors came to the eight large Percheron shows, including the state fairs at Illinois, Indiana, Michigan, Ohio, Pennsylvania and Wisconsin. The Chicago International cancelled its Percheron classes in the early 1950s.

When Ray Bast was elected President by the Association Board of Directors in 1965, the association had endured fifteen years of worsening business. From 1950 to 1965, fewer than 1,800 horses were registered. Bast remembered those lean years:

"This was the time when our large breeders, college professors and many breeders that are now breeders again, sold their Percherons saying this was the end of the draft horse.

"When we again started 'Percheron Notes', many of the people breeding Percherons — a few of which are still breeding Percherons today — would not give us $2 for a small ad.

"It was hard work but with Mrs. Brown's diligent help, and later Mr. and Mrs. Gossett, we started to come up slowly."[9]

The breeders who remained in the Percheron business during these years are largely responsible for the preservation of the breed. As fewer horses were bred, bloodlines suffered. The breeders of the day wisely bred discriminately, preserving the bloodlines of many of the greatest sires and dams of the 1920s, 30s and 40s.

Anne Brown Retires

When Anne Brown retired in 1965 as Secretary-Treasurer of the association, the officers began to search for a replacement.

"It had to be someone capable, also someone with facilities to store our equipment. It also had to be someone who had another source of income as this position could not pay much."[8]

Dale and Lucille Gossett and daughter Kay (middle).

Gossett Hired

A three-man committee recommended Dale Gossett as Secretary. Gossett, a longtime Percheron breeder, was hired with his wife, Lucille, as his assistant. During their tenure, the association's records and office equipment were kept in the Gossett's basement.

Dale Gossett served as Secretary until his death December 14, 1978, at which time his wife, Lucille, took over the reins as Secretary-Treasurer. During the late 1970s, the Percheron business had begun to pick up.

References

[1]Percheron News, July, 1949, p. 7.

[2]Percheron News, January, 1950, p. 5.

[3]Percheron News, July, 1949.

[4]Ray H. Bast, "Highlights of the Last Forty Years", Percheron Notes, 1984, p. 9.

[5]Percheron Notes, Spring, 1954, p. 5.

[6]Percheron Notes, April, 1952., p. 1.

[7]Association records.

[8]Bast, "Highlights of the Last Forty Years," Percheron Notes, 1984., p. 9.

[9]Letter from Ray Bast to author, April 15, 1991.

The Modern Association
(1981-1990)

When Lucille Gossett told the Association directors she wished to retire from the position of Secretary-Treasurer in 1980, the directors began to search for her replacement. At the same time, a majority of the directors felt that the Association offices should not be located in the home of the new Secretary, but should be housed in a new business office.

In 1981 the Association bought a plot in Fredericktown, Ohio, and built this one-story office building there. In front of the building, next to the Association sign, is the original stone which served as the grave marker for the Percheron stallion Laet.

Office Built in Fredericktown, Ohio

It was an optimistic time for the association. It had survived the lean years and now found itself with about $45,000 in the bank due both to the able leadership of President Ray Bast as well as to an increase in registration and transfer fees paid to the Association.

"In 1980 when Mrs. Gossett wanted to retire and we had accumulated a little money, I suggested to the Board of Directors that we could build a modest office, and hire a new secretary-treasurer. The directors were in full agreement and we proceeded.

"I think this was the best action our association ever took and our organization grew steadily and kept on growing and is still growing.[1]

The Association searched for a location for the new office. After exploring several locations — many sites were suggested by the various Association directors and members — the Association officers eventually decided to buy a plot in Fredericktown, Ohio, and build a new one-story building there.

Alex and Elaine Christian

Alex Christian Hired as Secretary

After interviewing three candidates for the job, a three-member committee hired Alex Christian, formerly of Radcliff, Ohio, to serve as Secretary-Treasurer, and his wife, Elaine, to work part-time as his assistant. As the office work grew, Elaine began working full time, and other part-time help was hired.

Among the tasks of the Secretary is the job of promoting the breed. Many of the Secretaries before Christian were natural-born salesmen, and Christian also fits that description. Under his direction the annual Percheron Notes — which was averaging about 50 pages in size — was changed back to the Percheron News, and published quarterly, with a total of more than 300 pages. Christian also revived the tradition, begun in the first half of the century, of visiting large horse shows

J. William Reed

and sales with a visitors' booth to promote the Percheron breed. He started a Percheron Calendar which has also helped cultivate interest in Percherons.

J. William Reed Elected President

At the 1983 Annual Meeting, Ray Bast, who had served as President of the Association since 1965, was not re-elected as a director and so was forced out as President as the officers are selected from among the Directors. At the reorganizational meeting of the Directors, J. William (Bill) Reed was elected President to succeed Bast.

Thus ended the Presidency of Ray Bast, who had guided the association through what were likely its most challenging years. During that time, Bast was forced to make many difficult decisions — decisions which worked to the Association's benefit but which also made Bast a number of enemies who ultimately conspired to overthrow him.

World Percheron Congress

The first World Percheron Congress was held in England in 1978. The second was featured in LeMans, France, in 1981. In 1983 the third Congress was held in Calgary, Alberta, Canada, hosted by the Canadian Percheron Association and with many

American Percheron breeders — both with and without their horses — attending the event. At the Calgary Congress, officials from the Canadian, British, French, Australian and American Percheron associations agreed to hold the fourth Congress in America. A World Congress Committee was formed among the members of the Percheron Horse Association of America to locate a site and do the preliminary planning for the event. In late 1984, after

The yearling mare class at the 1986 Percheron Congress.

many sites had been contacted and rejected (most of the preferred sites were unavailable) the Minnesota Percheron Club, under the direction of President Harold Schumacher and Secretary Judy Haroldson, made a proposal to have the Congress at the Minnesota Fairgrounds in St. Paul, Minn. The proposal was accepted, partly because there was a local club ready and willing to act as hosts for the event.

The Committee underwent several changes in personnel during the site selection process, but finally included Association Directors Bill Reed, Marilyn Robinson and Ralph Coddington, along with Robert Vickrey, Tom Berry, Bob Mischka, Harold Schumacher and Association Secretary Alex Christian. Bob Vickrey was elected Chairman of the group, and Bob Mischka was appointed Treasurer.

A budget was established for the event which was expected to cost well over $100,000. Fund raising was started by Mischka, as it was hoped that a corporate sponsor could be located to underwrite most of the expense. It soon became evident that the Percheron Association, with money in their treasury and more than 2,000 members, was not considered an appropriate recipient of limited corporate charitable funds. The burden of financing the Congress would have to be borne by the Association and its members.

Appeals were made to the membership to sponsor individual classes, and to make other donations to the Congress. These appeals were only marginally satisfactory. The Association had provided the Congress Committee with about $2,000 in "seed money" to begin their

Percheron Association Officials at the Congress Banquet included, left to right, Secretary Alex Christian and directors Jon Bast, Richard Lee, Abraham Allebach, Robert Vickrey, Marilyn Robinson, James Barnhart, J. William Reed, Marvyn Forwood and John Hay.

work, and had pledged the profit from their calendar sales, but had steadfastly opposed any direct committment of other Association funds for the Congress. The conservative nature of the Association Board of Directors on this subject can be best illustrated by noting that even those Directors who served on the Congress Committee voted against the use of Association funds when the subject was brought up at several Directors Meetings.

Congress Treasurer Mischka felt that if the Association was not willing to commit funds to the Congress that it was ridiculous to expect individual members and outside corporations to do so, and a final appeal was made by Vickrey and Mischka for financial and moral support from the Directors on November 1, 1985. A financial committment of $25,000 was requested. The Board finally agreed to contribute up to $15,000 to the Congress, if it was found to be necessary.

After a great deal of work, particularly on the part of Judy Haroldson and others from the Minnesota group, the Congress went on, as scheduled, July 17-22, 1986. Dave Haxton, son of Dave Haxton of Laet and Woodside Farm fame, and show chairman of the Ohio State Fair Draft Horse Show, was engaged as Congress Show Chairman.

The 1986 World Percheron Congress proved to be the largest single-breed draft horse show ever held. More than 400 Percherons were shown and breeders came from France, England, Australia, Canada and from all over the U.S. In the 1987 Percheron News, Secretary Christian reported that "there were 25 yearling stallions and 35 yearling mares shown. There were 21 brood mares, and the big surprise was the 16 aged stallions shown, a number unheard of in this day and age."[1]

At the Congress Banquet, past President Ray Bast was honored by the Association, some three years after he left office.

Past President Ray Bast was honored for his many years of service to the Percheron Horse Association during the banquet at the Congress. Pictured behind Bast is Congress Chairman Robert Vickrey.

Three seminars were held during the Congress. One discussed the legal aspects of horse ownership and another took up horse parasitism. The third seminar consisted of a

Blue Ribbon Panel featuring seven Percheron breeders, farriers, veterinarians, fitters and teachers. The seven were: Dennis Mays, Fredericksburg, Ohio, a professional horseshoer and successful Percheron breeder; Irvan Chamberlin, Semans, Saskatchewan, Canada, longtime Percheron breeder and author of several articles discussing changes in type; Dr. Richard Sears, Casenovia, NY, a veterinarian who raised Percherons and conducted draft horse clinics at Cornell University; Phillip Taylor, Smithfield, Maine, longtime Percheron and Belgian horseman, now retired, but who still judges at larger draft horse shows; Jesse Darlington, Boalsburg, Penn., another longtime Percheron breeder and showman; Jon Bast, Cocalalla, Idaho, still another Percheron breeder and showman and then director of the Percheron Association; and Richard Lee, Hilbert, Wis., yet another Percheron breeder, showman and association director.

The Panel discussed four aspects of the breed: Ideal Breed Type; Ideal Foot Shape and Size; Hocks and Hind-leg Set; and Sidebones.

In the end, the Percheron Congress' ending financial report showed that total income, including an amazing $17,000 from raffling a filly donated by Bob Vickrey, of $111,000 exceeded expenses by over $7,000 — without the $15,000 support pledged by the Association and without an estimated income of $3,000 from calendar sales also pledged to the Congress. These amounts not needed, plus the surplus, were placed in a separate bank account to accumulate interest to be used for a future Congress.

Vickrey Honored

Shortly after the Congress, Congress Chairman Robert Vickrey of Memphis, Mich., was elected to the Association Board of Directors and named Vice-President of the Association. In addition, Vickrey was honored as the 1986 Member of the Year at the Annual meeting of the Percheron Horse Association of America held October 31, 1986, in recognition to his service as Chairman of the Congress. Less than two years later, Bob Vickrey died on Feb. 14, 1988.

Robert L. Vickrey

Vickrey and his Belle River Farms had been a dominant force in the Percheron showring. During the show season before his death, his six-horse hitch of dapple grays, driven by his son, Robert S. Vickrey, had placed first at the Ohio State Fair at Columbus, the Great Lakes International at Detroit and the Royal Winter Fair at Toronto, Ontario, Canada — the three largest Percheron shows in North America.

The 1989 Percheron News was dedicated to the memory of Vickrey and featured a full-page tribute to him written by Secretary Christian:

"Bob Vickrey was in every sense of the word, a gentleman, a man of principal whose word was his bond. He had a keen sense of fair play, honesty and integrity. Bob set many of the standards by which I will measure future directors of our association. I have learned from him, and I am a better person and secretary having known him. I say this with all due respect to the other directors."[2]

At the association's annual meeting following his father's death, Robert S. Vickrey was elected to the Percheron Horse Association's Board of Directors.

Association Computerized

In 1985, the board of directors approved a recommendation to computerize the Percheron Horse Association's registration and other records. By mid-1987, the process had been completed. The entire changeover cost the association only about $15,000, a surprisingly small amount of money for such a large task. At the helm of the process was Tom Berry of Liberty, Mo.

"Tom Berry is doing the programming work, which will tailor the computers to our specific needs. Tom has put a great deal of time and resources into this program and were it not for his help I seriously doubt that we could afford to go through the changeover. The expertise and

Elaine Christian presents Ralph Coddington, Indianapolis, with the association's first computer-generated certificates of pedigree. Standing behind are Tom Berry, Liberty, Mo., who implemented the association's computer system, and Secretary Alex Christian.

resources which Tom has given our Association, we could not afford to buy."[3]

The first computer-generated certificate of pedigree was produced in May, 1987.

Tom Berry Elected President

When Bill Reed retired as president of the association at the annual meeting in November, 1989, after six years in that office, he nominated as his replacement Tom Berry. Berry, a relative newcomer to the Percheron horse industry, had come onto the scene quickly and enthusiastically.

"Tom got into the Percheron business in the spring of 1983. I met him later that summer when he made a quick trip to Ohio to look for horses. Tom quickly became an important part of our association. He attended all our meetings and offered his help in several areas including printing the first Percheron Stud Book since 1938. When this was completed, Tom started working on computer programs which would modernize all our office operations.

Association President Tom Berry

"Tom was an essential part of our World Congress Committee when the Congress was held in St. Paul in 1986. That fall, he was elected to the Board of Directors. He has worked closely with our Board and my office since the beginning, and helped us in so many phases of our operation that I can't even begin to tell you about."[4]

Association Enters 1990s

In the 1990 Percheron News, Christian brings the members up to date with the association business over the past decade:

"Our Association was growing. With the new

A portion of the Percheron Horse Association of America's display at the 1986 World Congress.

leadership in the office of the President, our Committees began to function. The Officers and Directors began taking a more active role in the operations of the Association. Changes were made, improvements and mistakes were made. I like to believe we've corrected most of our mistakes and expanded on the improvements. I am sure we will make many more, both improvements and mistakes.

"We were given the opportunity by the World organization to hold the 1986 World Congress. With the help of our membership, we pulled it off with great success. During this period our offices were expanded, modernized and computerized. We now have complete control of the Percheron News publication with new typesetting computers which allows us to do all but the actual printing in our offices. In this past ten years, the 56-page Percheron Notes of 1980 has expanded to the Percheron News quarterly, just under 300 pages in 1989."[5]

The task of the Percheron Horse Association of America in the years ahead will be to promote the Percheron among hobbyists who use draft horses for recreation rather than as work horses on the farm, Christian wrote:

"It is unlikely that the scope of change seen the past ten years will be repeated in the near future. Yet the more we change, the more we look like the Association of the past. Until the great depression in the draft horse industry, the Percheron Horse Association was the undisputed leader in the purebred livestock industry in this country. Many of the ideas we come up with, such as large promotional displays at sales and shows, are not new. This was the norm before the big bust. We can learn by looking backward as well as forward.

"As we enter the decade of the 1990s, the future looks bright for our breed and our Association. Our future depends more on the economy of the country in general, than it does on the farm economy and the need for work horses on the farm, as it did only a few decades ago. While the work horse is by no means a thing of the past, much of our future lies in the hobbyist and in the recreational use of the draft horse."[6]

Indeed, the draft horse industry stands upon an entirely different economic foundation than it had forty years before. Today, it is a difficult thing to make a living breeding, raising and selling draft horses — of any breed. Most people involved in heavy horses have other occupations which help them afford to keep and show their drafters.

References

[1] Letter from Ray Bast to author, April 15, 1991.

[2] Percheron News, 1987, p. 43.

[3] Percheron News, January 1988, p. 5.

[4] Percheron News, March, 1987., p. 7.

[5] Percheron News, January, 1990., p. 11.

[6] Percheron News, January, 1990., p. 9.

[7] Ibid.

Prominent Figures
of the Day

*Some of the Horses and People
Responsible for the Development
of the Percheron Breed*

Oaklawn Farm and Brilliant

(1865 - 1931)

If no man can be said to be the "father" of the Percheron breed, then Mark W. Dunham of the Oaklawn farm of Wayne, Ill., certainly served as "midwife" to the American Percheron industry.

Brilliant — Sire of the Breed

Dunham is credited with being the first Percheron breeder to consistently raise large numbers of quality domestic Percherons. He also imported the stallion which later became the true foundation sire of the breed in America.

Among the Percherons found in America today, nearly all can be traced back to Brilliant 1271, foaled in 1877 and imported by Dunham as a four–year-old in 1881.

The son of Brilliant 1899, Brilliant 1271 stood at stud at Oaklawn Farm for 15 years, servicing "probably the greatest group of draft mares ever assembled by one breeder."[1]

The horse was described in an 1882 Oaklawn catalog:

"Weight 1,850; 16 hands high. Long and very round body; extraordinary length of quarters, which are broad and level; very sloping shoulders of unusual depth; neck rather short; medium throttle; fine ear; wide between the eyes; slightly Roman nose; very broad breast; short legs and bone of uncommon width; good feet; immense stifle power. A horse with a combination of excellencies throughout."[2]

Shortly after bringing Brilliant 1271 to the U.S., Dunham went back to France and imported 30 of the stallion's foals.

Brilliant 1899, also known as "Old Brilliant," the sire of Brilliant 1271, himself sired a number of well-received horses while in France. After being imported in 1881 by Leonard Johnson of East Castle Rock, Minn., Old Brilliant sired three purebred foals before being sold to P.C. Fockler a year later for $2,000.

Unfortunately, Fockler bred Old Brilliant to only grade mares during the fifteen years he owned him. When the horse was 30 years old, he became partially paralyzed in his hindquarters and required assistance to be lifted to his feet after resting — Fockler had him killed in 1897.

It is important to note that while Brilliant 1271 is known to have been a "most impressive horse in his general bearing, (as well as a) vigorous, supermasculine stallion,"[3] he was soon surpassed by his progeny in terms of quality, especially when the stallion was bred to mares sired by his father, Brilliant 1899.

Domestic Breeding Established

Dunham, who was known as one of America's leading importers of his time (from 1872 to 1880, he imported more than 300 stallions and 75 mares) was probably better known as an expert Percheron breeder. Between 1872 and 1900, 385 mares and 353 stallions (a total of 738 Percherons) were foaled at

This depiction of the famous stallion Brilliant, center, and a some of his offspring was painted by Frank Whitney and commissioned by Mark W. Dunham. The painting, entitled "The Thunder Storm," first appeared in a supplement to one of the annual holiday issues of "The Breeder's Gazette." It now hangs in the dining room of the Dunham-Hunt Country Club, part of the original Dunham farm.

Mark Dunham understood the value of advertising very well. Throughout his career as a Percheron breeder, Dunham commissioned several artists to depict his horses and farm, held many special events at his large estate, and had bulletins and circulars advertising his farm spread throughout the U.S. and parts of Europe. The advertisement pictured here appeared in the September, 1883, issue of the National Livestock Journal.

OAKLAWN FARM,

The Greatest Importing and Breeding Establishment in the World.

PERCHERON HORSES.

WORTH 2,500,000·00,

Imported from France, and Bred, since 1872, by

M. W. DUNHAM,

Wayne, Du Page County,

ILLINOIS.

35 miles west of Chicago, on C. & N. W. R'y.

IMP. VIDOCQ No. 451.

390 Imported from France the past Three Months,

consisting only of the FINEST ANIMALS, with CHOICEST PEDIGREES, REGISTERED in the PERCHERON STUD BOOK of FRANCE, and the PERCHERON-NORMAN STUD BOOK of the UNITED STATES.

Visitors welcome. Come and see for yourselves. **Prices low for quality of stock, and every stallion guaranteed a breeder.**

Carriage at depot. Telegraph at Wayne, with private telephone connection with Oaklawn.

Oaklawn — all this at a time when most Percheron men felt the only good Percherons could be had overseas and so were importing most pureblood animals from the Perche. Dunham, too, imported horses from France and was well-respected for his abilities in choosing animals there. Yet, the quality of the stock raised at Oaklawn often surpassed those he bought overseas.

"It must be remembered that purchasers going there (Oaklawn) had the opportunity of making selections from a large number of high–class imported horses or from the colts bred at Oaklawn; the fact that so many (buyers) bought colts bred and raised there, at good prices, is evidence of the high character of the progeny."[4]

Dunhams Come to Illinois

The youngest of eleven children, Mark was born June 22, 1842, the son of Solomon and Lydia Dunham who came to Illinois from their home in Erie County, New York, in March 1835. Mark was born and raised on the 300-acre farm his father bought on May 8, 1835, and which was to become Oaklawn Farm.

Solomon was widely respected for his strong convictions and unyielding will. He was made one of the county's first commissioners, in June, 1836, and was the first County Assessor. He served on the first grand jury in the county and was the first station agent and postmaster at Wayne. He also worked as surveyor for the Galena and Chicago Railroad.

Accompanying Solomon on his trip west, Mark Wentworth Fletcher settled in nearby Geneva. M.W. Fletcher married Solomon's daughter, Harriet, in 1846. Years later, Fletcher's grandson, James Fletcher, would become an associate of Mark Dunham, and later Wirth Dunham, in the horse business.

Although Solomon knew little about horses and was not especially interested in Percherons, he developed a keen interest in the breeding and raising of other farm stock. After his father's death in 1865, Mark Dunham, then 23 years old, continued this tradition of raising quality livestock.[5]

Mark Dunham

Mark Dunham Begins Importing

Mark Dunham realized that the agricultural innovations of the day such as the McCormick Reaper, would increase the demand for strong, heavy horses. In the mid-1860s Mark went to Europe, visiting England, Belgium and France, and decided to import the farm's first Percheron horse, Success, from France. By 1873, Mark had imported another 23 stallions and four mares.

Noted French Percheron breeder Edmond Perriot, who during the Paris Exposition of 1900 sold $100,000 worth of horses to American breeders, remembered Mark Dunham during the 1870s and 1880s:

"One of my earliest recollections is that of seeing Mark Dunham who came over here to buy every year. That was long before the stud book was known here, when horses could be shipped to America without pedigree. Mr. Dunham came here for 20 years, buying from 100 to 150 head annually. He was a keen judge and only wanted the best, for which he was willing to pay a good price. From the very beginning, prices have been relatively high for good breeding stock, and Mr. Dunham did not hesitate, even in the early days, to go as high as $3,000 and even $5,000 for the horse he wanted."[6]

Mark Dunham is pictured standing behind some French Percheron breeders. Dunham visited France each year for 20 years to select horses to import to the U.S. He continued to import French horses even after he had begun producing his own Percherons at his Wayne, Ill., farm. Dunham earned a reputation of being an honest businessman who always paid fair prices.

Troubles with Large-Scale Breeding

Oaklawn Farm soon became the largest influence on the Percheron breed in the U.S. With a large herd of broodmares — the bulk of which were imported from France — Oaklawn began breeding horses on a large scale. Shortly after beginning the venture, however, the farm ran into difficulty.

"The troubles which forever beset breeders of draft horses who try to do things in a wholesale way soon made their appearance. Mr. Dunham raised 31 colts foaled in 1883, but the following spring when he had approximately 150 mares, a large proportion of them of breeding age, he raised but 13 colts. Abortion tells the story. In 1885 he reared 32 colts from 150 eligible mares, and in 1886, got but 20. Probably the mares were in too high condition. Anyhow they did not as a rule conceive for the first two or three years after importation and the foals produced by those that did breed were inclined to be so lacking in vitality that the mortality rate was extremely high."[7]

Shortly thereafter, Mark began maintaining smaller groups of mares and started working those mares on the farm to keep them in better condition for foaling. From then on, Oaklawn mares began raising foals with greater frequency and regularity.

It was the combination of having the most prepotent Percheron stallions as well as sound horse-

Photo Courtesy of Rahr-West Art Museum, Manitowoc, Wis.

Isadore Bonheur, brother of painter Rosa Bonheur, sculpted this bronze of Brilliant 1271 for the Dunham family.

raising practices, that caused Oaklawn Farm to profoundly influence the Percheron breeding industry in America.

"One of the leading features of Mr. Dunham's work at this time was its effect on others. He demonstrated conclusively that Percherons paid. He proved that Percherons could be bred in America, and sold at early ages and high prices...He advertised early and late, more freely and with better results than any horseman of his own or earlier times, and he popularized Percherons on the soundest of all platforms — their utility value on the farm, and their ability to raise the value of common horses from one-fourth to one-third by the first cross, and to continue raising the market value by each subsequent cross."[8]

Sells Horses During Depression

Even during the economic depression which suppressed most industries in America, including the Percheron business, Mark continued to sell horses, and inspired other Percheron breeders to stay the course.

"When other men could not sell Percherons, or sold at ridiculously low prices, Mr. Dunham inspired confidence in the final outcome, encouraged many men to hold on, and was successful in making sales at good prices...He had faith, enthusiasm, foresight, and a knowledge of human nature which made him more than ever a commanding figure in the business when others had failed to weather the storm."[9]

Oaklawn was the largest importing and breeding horse farm in the world during its time. As the horse business became more successful, Mark Dunham built Dunham Castle in the early 1880s. Patterned after a French chateau he had seen on one of his trips to Normandy, the palatial home featured a 3-1/2 story tower on its southeast corner.

The farm itself was a showcase. With approximately five barns, the farm featured the most recent advances in livestock production.

"Oaklawn Stables present a solid front of 660 feet — one-eighth of a mile — and the barns are models in their way. The buildings are as complete as man's ingenuity can make them, and are, in themselves, worth a day's journey to examine."[10]

Himself a world traveller, Dunham hosted many domestic and foreign dignitaries. In 1889, representatives to the International Conference of American States visited Oaklawn.

*"The run to Wayne, a distance of thirty-five miles (from Chicago),
was made in forty-three minutes. At the station, the guests were
seated in carriages and driven to Mr. Dunham's residence, about a
mile from the station. Mr. M.W. Dunham's farm, known as 'Oaklawn,'
is one of the largest and most completely equipped in the country; it
covers about 1,700 acres and is a model in every particular."*[11]

Dunham Dies in 1899

Mark Dunham died of blood-poisoning in 1899 at age 53.
(Some have reported Dunham contracted the poisoning after
treating a horse's sore foot.) Dunham's early passing was unfor-
tunate for the Percheron industry; the political turmoil following
the turn of the century — as Percheron breeders split into three
individual camps for political reasons — would likely have been
averted or at least lessened had Dunham lived longer.

Photo Courtesy of Jane Dunham

In the early 1880s,
Mark Dunham built
Dunham Castle
outside Wayne, Ill.
The building was
fashioned after a
French chateau
Dunham had visited
during a one of his
many trips to France.
The building is well
preserved today and
at the time of this
writing, is owned as a
private residence.

Son Wirth Takes Over Operation

The heir to the Oaklawn throne was Dunham's son, Wirth, who was 21 years old and finishing law school at Harvard. Mark Dunham's will requested that Wirth should take as partners into the selling organization James M. Fletcher, the elder Dunham's nephew, and C.R. Coleman, who had worked for many years as an Oaklawn salesman. Wirth Dunham would maintain control over the farm and breeding operations, however. Although the will left the farm to Wirth, he divided it equally with his two sisters.

Shortly after his return to Wayne, Wirth married Mary Louise Ward. They had two daughters, Barbara in 1902 and Jane in 1906.

When the Duke of Veragua, a descendent of Columbus, visited the U.S., he stopped at the Oaklawn Farm. The Chicago Herald ran this drawing of the Duke stopping in nearby Wayne with its story about the event.

In 1915, Wirth was asked to head the Midwest Section of the Remount (to secure horses for the cavalry, artillery and general Army transportation) until his honorable discharge in December 1919, as a Major.

The past success of his father was not quickly forgotten by Wirth as evidenced by the prominent treatment of his father's photograph in a 1916 catalogue, and the words:

"It must be remembered that Oaklawn's history is most intimately interwoven with that of the Percheron horse. Forty-six years ago Percheron breeding began here. Forty years ago the late M.W. Dunham made that epoch-making importation of seven stallions, which marks the beginning of the pure-bred horse business on a commercial scale in the United States."[12]

Farm is Sold

The farm continued to prosper until the late 1920s when Wirth, then a Director of the Percheron Horse Society and President of the newly-formed Horse Association of America, held a dispersal sale of 35 Percherons in February, 1929. In a half-page advertisement in the 1929 *Percheron Review*, the family stated "The only reason we are going out of the Percheron business is because we are selling the pasture land on our farm for real estate subdivision purposes."

Wirth was later killed when the automobile he was driving was struck by a drunken driver in 1931.

Rosa Bonheur

Mark Dunham knew well the value of promotion. He advertised his operation through circulars, posters and livestock journal advertisements and encouraged other breeders of the day to do likewise.

But since the technology to reproduce photographs on a large scale was still in its infancy, Dunham had to rely on artists' drawings of his animals to show prospective buyers what his horses looked like.

Wirth Dunham

Rosa Bonheur

Because he believed he owned some of the finest Percheron horses in America, Dunham felt he needed the best portraits of those animals to be used in his advertising.

Perhaps the best horse artist alive at that time was Rosa Bonheur.

In 1853, when only 31 years old, Rosa Bonheur displayed her masterpiece "The Horse Fair" and won international acclaim. The painting was later published widely in America, helping to promote the Percheron breed.

Dunham sent his associate Samuel D. Thompson, to Paris in the late spring of 1885 to speak to Bonheur about painting several Oaklawn horses, including Brilliant.

Thompson was to have a copy of the French society's stud book specially bound and inscribed by society officials, and then to present the book to Bonheur as a gift, probably

Rosa Bonheur's painting, "The Horse Fair", painted in 1853, is probably the most famous depiction of Percheron horses.

to soften Bonheur before Thompson made his pitch. (Thompson later became the Percheron Horse Society's Secretary around the turn-of-the-century.)

Thompson related how things were going in a letter to M.W. Dunham dated July 22, 1885:

"You may perhaps think I am a long time in writing you about the Rosa Bonheur offer but I assure you it was no easy matter to accomplish. But as you have already been informed by telegram, I have succeeded in getting you what you want. Upon receipt of your first telegram I immediately had a copy of the second volume of the stud book put up in a costly and handsome binding with an inscription on the cover 'offered by The Societé Hippique Percheronne as a grateful tribute to Mademoiselle Rosa Bonheur.'"

Thompson then included with the book a letter from him asking to meet with Bonheur:

"I received a most gracious answer assuring me that she would be most happy to receive me and appointing the day. She sent her carriage to the train for me and received me most graciously. By degrees, I brought the conversation around to a request for three more sketches. At first it looked rather blue, she saying that it was simply impossible to accept any more work this year. But I am not the fellow to give up so easily and used my powers of persuasion to such good advantage that at last I had the pleasure of hearing her say 'In the face of such arguments, I feel I cannot refuse Mr. Thompson his request.' She then said she would invite me when to send the horses."

Bonheur's famous portrait of Oaklawn's stallion Brilliant .

Photo Courtesy of Carol Burt Rogers

At this point, Thompson related to his boss, things began to become complicated.

"After a few days [I] received a message from you to 'make desperate effort to have her make Brilliant family group instead of those promised'. Now this was a poser for I was fearful that by asking a change I would kick the whole thing over, she being very nervous and fidgety — but for you to command is for me to do. So I sat myself to thinking how to do it. It may perhaps look easy to you but if you knew her and knew how much tact I had to use to get her consent to the first arrangement you would believe me when I say that I laid awake more than one night thinking over the matter. I said nothing about it until I received her letter yesterday, telling me to bring on the horses."

Thompson then met with Bonheur explaining to her Dunham's wishes, and telling her of the significance of the Brilliant family in America. Bonheur consented to the change.

"Just as I was leaving her I think I made a big point. She was telling me that she was looking up American Indian costumes as she was going to paint an Indian picture. She asked me if I knew anything about the wild mustang of the west. I, of course, told her

Another of Bonheur's portraits of Oaklawn Percherons including Brilliant 1271 in the center.

I knew all about them. She said if she could only get one she would be happy. I immediately told her that nothing would afford me greater pleasure than to have one caught in America and sent over to her. She became at once enchanted and asked if it was really possible that I could procure her a veritable wild mustang. I, of course, pledged my word that she should have a veritable one next year. That you would have one caught and taken to Oaklawn where it would be tamed and sent to her next spring. Now perhaps I was a little premature but as I have promised it you will have to carry it out.

"I fancy I see a bit of advertising in it for instead of letting her pay for it you might write her a nice letter asking her to accept it as a present (I know she would accept it). She would then write you a personal letter and I feel confident that I could so arrange it that she would pay you a glowing tribute as the one who has done so much in America for the Percheron race. At any rate, it won't cost very much and I think you will not regret it."

Dunham Sends Mustangs to Bonheur

Dunham fulfilled Thompson's promise to Bonheur, sending her three wild mustangs in 1886. Bonheur thanked Dunham in a letter dated October 28, 1886. Translated, it reads:

"I write to thank you with all my heart for the very great pleasure you have given me — so courteously and generously — by the gift of the three wild horses of the prairies which were brought to me.The true and good service you render me, sir, is for me, to have the types of the horses the Indians used and use still when they go out hunting the buffaloes and wild horses of the prairies; a very interesting subject for me;."

The St. Charles (Ill.) Chronical wrote the following story in 1887:

"Those wild American horses which were for some time at Oaklawn, St. Charles Township, have reached their destination and will be made famous by reproduction on the canvas by the greatest animal painter of the world. They were selected from herds on the plains by Mr. Dunham, at the request of the artist, who desired to picture the untamed horse. . . . . Rosa Bonheur is delighted with them, and intends using them as models for a large American cattle picture. She in return presented Mr. Dunham and Colonel Thompson with three exquisite portraits of Percheron

stallions, selected by Rosa Bonheur herself from a considerable number purchased by Mr. Dunham."

From that early incident, a relationship of mutual respect evolved between the French painter and Dunham. In a letter to a member of the French Society dated July 17, 1889, Bonheur — having just suffered the loss of her longtime companion Nathalie Micas — described Dunham.

"I thank you heartily for your good letter and the words of kindness you express to me in the great grief which is striking me.

"I thank you also — and wish you would thank for me Mr. Dunham — for the so good words he has pronounced when speaking of me at the Banquet of La Ferté Bernard.

"There is in Mr. Dunham the heart of a just man and a loyal man who remembers that I may have been the innocent cause of making Percherons known in America."[13]

Bonheur completed several works for Dunham, including a fine drawing of a group of Oaklawn horses with Brilliant 1271 standing in the center.

References

[1]Alvin Howard Sanders and Wayne Dinsmore, <u>A History of the Percheron Horse</u>, (Sanders Publishing Co., 1917), p. 240.

[2]Ibid., p. 241.

[3]Ibid., p. 241.

[4]Ibid., p. 245-46.

[5]Ibid., p. 161.

[6]Ibid., p. 217.

[7]Ibid., p. 244.

[8]Ibid., pp. 254-55.

[9]Ibid., p. 255.

[10]Elgin Advocate, February 12, 1881.

[11]American Breeder, October, 1889.

[12]1916 Oaklawn Stud Book Catalog.

[13]Letters from S.D. Thompson and Rosa Bonheur, the collection of Miss Jane Dunham, Geneva, Ill.

White, Butler & Laet

(1916-1936)

O ne of the Percheron breed's most successful and influential
stallions, both in terms of his own individual success as well
as the records of his progeny, was Laet 133886.

Laet was bred on E.B. White's Selma, Va., farm and then later
sold to W.H. Butler of Woodside, Ohio. The two men were good
friends and held one another in great regard.

Laet was called the
"Sire of Sires", a
title still attributed
to him today.

Photo Courtesy of Cook & Gormley

LAET
GRAND CHAMPION STALLION INTERNATIONAL 1921
GRAND CHAMPION STALLION OHIO STATE FAIR 1919

When Society President White fell ill in the fall of 1925 and was unable to attend the Annual Meeting of the Society in November of that year, Vice President W. H. Butler of Woodside Farms, Columbus, Ohio, extolled White's virtues:

"I know of no one man in America who has done more for the Percheron horse than E. B. White, not only giving valiant service as president of your Society, but as a breeder of worthwhile Percherons as well."

Butler's remarks were soon followed by those of Society Director W. S. Corsa of Whitehall, Ill.:

"Those of us who recall the trying times through which we have all been, with President White leading, guiding, and encouraging us on, view the present so far as the standing of the association is concerned with great confidence for the future. He has been a mainstay to us in his wisdom and in his hopefulness. The finances of the Association are at a point which, I take it, have not heretofore been approached."

E.B. White Dies

When White died a year later Dec. 17, 1926, Society Secretary Ellis McFarland wrote a full-page tribute honoring him in the 1927 Percheron Review:

"He is the man to whom belongs the credit, more than anyone else, for the present high standing which the Percheron Society of America holds among other record associations for its clean records. When lawsuits threatened the destruction of the Society, Col. White never wavered for one moment in his attitude that if we could not keep our records free from fraud, we might as well not have a Percheron Society. Every other breed of purebred livestock owes a debt of gratitude to this man for the stand which he made on this all important principle of integrity."

White began breeding Percherons in 1903 after purchasing a pair of mares from the Hartman Stock Farm of Columbus. He then

E.B. White

became Society President a scant ten years later. Of the about 150 Percherons produced during the 23 years he was in business, his greatest achievement was the founding of the famous Laet family. A portrait of White was the first to be selected to hang in the Percheron Society's Hall of Fame in December 1935.

Laet's Show Record

Foaled in 1916, Laet's show record stands as a testimonial to the horse's influence:

- He sired 9 of the 13 stallions named Grand Champion at the Chicago International in from 1923 to 1936.

Couceorous (at left), dam of Laet, and her two grand champion sons, Treviso and Laet (at right). E.B. White bought Couceorous from John Buswell for $2,000 in 1913 after seeing the horse as a yearling filly at the Iowa State Fair.

- He was named Premier Sire of Breed 6 times from 1928 to 1936.
- He won Champion Get-of-Sire at the Chicago International nine times from 1922 to 1936.

White Buys Laet's Dam

Laet was the product of careful breeding, as related by D.J. Kays, Secretary of the Ohio Percheron Breeder's Association in the late 1920s:

"In 1913, the late Col. E.B. White was judging Percherons at the Iowa State Fair at Des Moines. John Buswell of Bradford, Ill., had shipped a small exhibit of Percherons to the Hawkeye Fair that year. Included in his show string was a black yearling filly, big and rugged, sound and growthy, a young mare that evidenced outcome. Mr. White liked her. He placed her in blue ribbon position among the yearling fillies. He made her Junior Champion. He made her Grand Champion, and before the week had ended, to prove to folks that he really liked this champion mare, whose name was Couceorous, he gave John Buswell $2,000 for her, with shipping instructions to send her to Selma Farm.

"I have often heard the Senator describe this fascinating bit of Percheron experience. He said, 'I wanted this big, strong, deep bodied filly because I thought she looked like she would have room to develop a good sized colt before it was foaled. I figured that by crossing her on a medium sized tight made horse, I could produce stallions big enough that buyers would be willing to pay long prices for.' "[1]

White bred Couceorous to a variety of his stallions, including Seducteur and Dragon. Those breeding combinations netted White three Ohio State Fair Champions. Laet, by Seducteur, was named grand champion stallion in 1919. Treviso, by Dragon, won the prize in 1921 and Giroust II, by Giroust, was named grand champion stallion in 1923.

W. H. Butler

While many of Couceorous' offspring — and, later, their own sons and daughters — found great success in the show and auction rings, none were as influential as Laet.

White raised the horse, but sold him — as well as some of Selma Farm's best broodmares — when Laet was three years old and shown only once, at the 1919 Ohio State Fair where he was named Grand Champion Stallion.

Butler Buys Laet

W.H. Butler, of Woodside Farms, Columbus, Ohio, bought Laet the day after he won Grand Champion. The conversation between the two men, White and Butler, is documented in a booklet, "Laet, Sire of Sires," produced by Elizabeth H. Butler:

"The day following the banquet, the Colonel and Mr. Butler were coming down through the little arena in the horse barns at the state fair. In characteristic fashion, E.B. put his arm around his friend's shoulders and said:

'My boy, do you want to buy that horse of mine?'

'Yes, I do,' was the reply. 'What will you take for him — but wait a minute,' and Mr. Butler stopped his friend, 'I don't want him unless you will sell me some mares to go with him and will permit me to select them.'

'What mares do you want?' asked Mr. White, who often said that he would sell anything but his wife.

Mr. Butler named them, and they were the very heart of the Virginia Colonel's herd — mares whose individuality and breeding were of the highest character. Four of them were by the Colonel's famous herd sire, Dragon.

'My conscience,' ejaculated Mr. White, 'that would take the cream of my herd. You would be getting twenty years of my breeding operations.'

'That's true, was the reply, 'but I haven't a mare at Woodside fit to breed that horse to.'"[2]

Butler Hires Dave Haxton

Three years prior to Laet's arrival at Woodside Farm, Butler hired Dave Haxton in October, 1916. A native of Kinross, Scotland, Dave Haxton was the

Dave Haxton

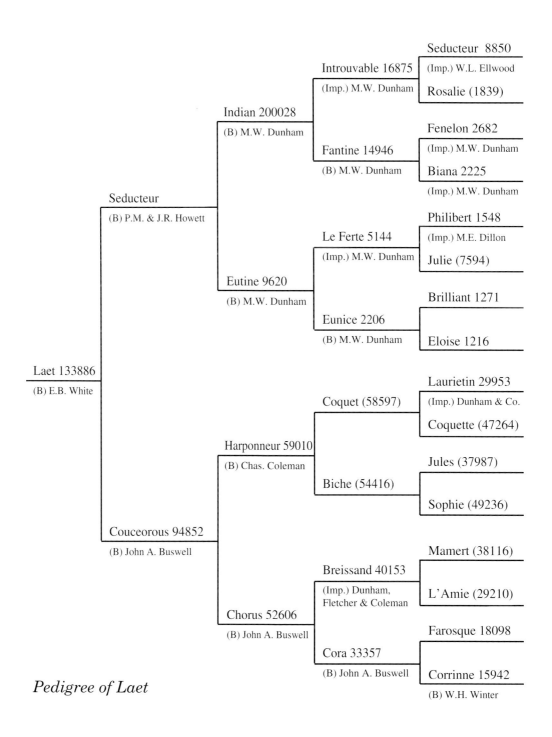

Pedigree of Laet

Laet 133886
(B) E.B. White

Seducteur
(B) P.M. & J.R. Howett

Couceorous 94852
(B) John A. Buswell

Indian 200028
(B) M.W. Dunham

Eutine 9620
(B) M.W. Dunham

Harponneur 59010
(B) Chas. Coleman

Chorus 52606
(B) John A. Buswell

Introuvable 16875
(Imp.) M.W. Dunham

Fantine 14946
(B) M.W. Dunham

Le Ferte 5144
(Imp.) M.W. Dunham

Eunice 2206
(B) M.W. Dunham

Coquet (58597)

Biche (54416)

Breissand 40153
(Imp.) Dunham,
Fletcher & Coleman

Cora 33357
(B) John A. Buswell

Seducteur 8850
(Imp.) W.L. Ellwood

Rosalie (1839)

Fenelon 2682
(Imp.) M.W. Dunham

Biana 2225
(Imp.) M.W. Dunham

Philibert 1548
(Imp.) M.E. Dillon

Julie (7594)

Brilliant 1271

Eloise 1216

Laurietin 29953
(Imp.) Dunham & Co.

Coquette (47264)

Jules (37987)

Sophie (49236)

Mamert (38116)

L'Amie (29210)

Farosque 18098

Corrinne 15942
(B) W.H. Winter

third generation of good horsemen. He came to Canada in 1911 and spent some time with Alex Galbraith of Edmonton, Alberta. Galbraith is often said to have been responsible for bringing more good draft horses into Canada than any other man in the business at the time. Haxton also worked for the Canadian Remount Service, buying horses for the Canadian government.

Haxton, regarded by many as one of America's greatest draft horse fitters and showmen, was on the scene when Laet and seven of White's best Percheron mares were purchased. The mares included Laet's dam, Couceorous 94852, Syncopatian 113966, Iona 123962, Intrepid 131826, Perfection 123001, La Belle 34982, and Belle Dragon 131823. The sale of Laet and the seven mares was heralded as "the greatest transaction in the history of Percherons," by *The Breeders Gazette*, one of the leading livestock journals of the day.

Photo Courtesy of Cook & Gormley

A head shot of Laet, the Sire of Sires.

Haxton remembered seeing Laet for the first time after the horse was unloaded with White's other animals at the 1919 Ohio State Fair:

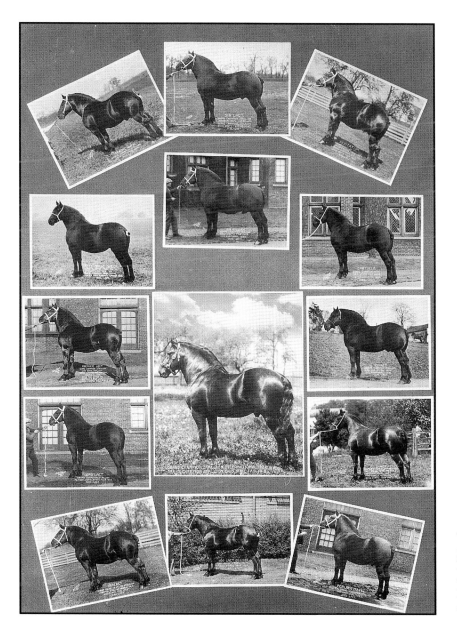

This montage of photographs shows Laet — in the center — with thirteen of his sons and daughters.

"There he stood, his head high, looking around that strange barn. It had been his first ride on a train. Everything was odd and new to him. I can still see the picture, his bold, masculine appearance, his smart little ear flicking this way and that, his high crest, his beautiful top and spring of rib, his great size, a trifle narrow when viewed from the front, but when viewed from the rear I had never seen one like him before, nor have I seen one since, his loin and hind quarters, his perfect set of hind legs, his grand flat wide hock. That hock interested me a lot, for I knew that this colt, more or less gangling at this time, would have to be fitted and heavily fed for a few years during his show career. I knew, however, that those hocks would stand the test, and they did, for I had the pleasure of fitting him prior to that memorable day when he was made grand champion at Chicago with his son Jerome reserve to him, an event which has never occurred since, a sire and his son, winning grand and reserve grand."[3]

The blood of Laet can be found in a great number of winning Percherons today. For example, Drake Farm's Chief, a very influential stallion of the 1950s and 60s, was a great-great-grandson of Laet.

Nine of his offspring won a total of 13 Grand Champions at the Chicago International. They included Hesitation, Laet's Magic

This stone marker for Laet's grave was retrieved from the old Woodside Farm in 1986 by Association officials. Since the original bronze plaque had been stolen in years past, the Association had an exact duplicate made, and the entire marker today rests in front of the Association offices in Fredericktown, Ohio.

Queen, Sir William, Jerome, Premier Laet, Carthela, Sir Laet, Cy Laet, and Milaet.

Laet Put Down

On the morning of December 22, 1936, Laet, suffering from poor digestion and bearing a cancerous growth on a hind leg, was put down at the age of 20. Dave Haxton, in an article he wrote for *The Draft Horse Journal*, August 1967, related the story of the great horse's passing:

"One of our neighbors owned a pair of geldings (sons of Laet). We had them brought forward with a plow and a teamscraper and put to work digging a large pit. Mr. Butler and his family had left for Florida. I had arranged with Dr. Walter R. Krill, our young veterinarian, to come on the morning of December 22, 1936.

"At 7:30 in the morning, we brushed his mane over, cleaned him up, fitted on his purple show blanket with gold lettering and binding (the Woodside colors). This was the one he wore leaving the ring the day he was Grand Champion at the 1921 International. Tom Wells led him toward the high mound on the hill by the Sycamore tree, but I left in the opposite direction.

"Upon my return two hours later, the team had worked up a sweat and the trench was almost filled. Somehow that Sycamore looked bigger that day; Perfection, Syncopation, La Belle and Rozelle were all asleep under its great branches and falling leaves."[4]

References

[1]"Some Sidelights on Buying Percherons," <u>The Percheron Review</u>, (1928), p. 10.

[2]<u>Laet, Sire of Sires,</u> written for Elizabeth H. Butler.

[3]Ibid, p. 18.

[4]<u>Draft Horse Journal,</u> August, 1967, Waverly, Iowa, p. 17.

Lynnwood Farm & Don Again

(1931-1954)

Don Again 206636 was foaled Feb. 16, 1931 on George A. Dix's Pentoila Farm in Delaware, Ohio. Don Again, the son of two-time International Grand Champion Stallion Don Degas, was owned by Dix, who served as President of the Association from 1953 to 1955 and was awarded the Achievement Breeder Award in 1937.

In December, 1936, Dix sold Don Again to Charles J. Lynn of Lynnwood Farm, Carmel, Ind., one of America's most influential Percheron breeders

Don Again 206636, bred by George Dix of Ohio and owned by Charles Lynn of Indiana, was a very prepotent sire for his time. Don Again was Premier Sire of the Percheron breed four times between 1939 and 1951.

Photo Courtesy of Cook & Gormley

Don Again was Premier Sire of the Percheron breed from 1939 to 1941 and again in 1951. His progeny were consistent winners at the largest national Percheron shows for many years. An advertisement in the March, 1938, issue of *The Draft Horse*, Lynn ran the following item:

"For the first time in 30 years a Percheron sire and his son won first and second in the Get of Sire Class at the 1937

George A. Dix

Charles J. Lynn

The Get of Don Degas at left includes Mar Dona, Don Again and Donilles. The Get of Don Again at right includes Fritzi, Marshall Murat and Betty Ann Degas. These two get of sires took First and second at the 1937 International.

Chicago International. In that First Prize Get of Sire group was our herd stallion Don Again 206636 whose get, in turn, stood second in the same class. As far back as records can be searched, this has never happened before at the International.

"Don Degas 186172, the sire of Don Again, already twice grand champion at the Chicago International and the sire of more top winners in 1936 than any other stallion of the breed, won the coveted honor — First Prize Get of Sire at the International — with Don Again in the group.

"This establishes for the Don Degas strain which carries the blood line of the great Carnot 66666 that tremendous carrying power called prepotency. Don Again is the only stallion whose colts won Get of Sire classes at three of the major shows in 1937. He has worn the royal purple and the blue out of the show ring many times.

"Breed your registered Percheron mares this season to Don Again whose get are winning high awards wherever shown."

In addition to Carnot, Don Again can be traced back to Laet, his great-grandfather on the side of his dam, the mare Hesitate Again, a daughter of the stallion Hesitation, an International Grand Champion himself.

The Lynnwood Farm, Carmel, Indiana.

Photo Courtesy of Cook & Gormley

One of Don Again's most successful sons was Lynnwood Don who was named Grand Champion Stallion at the 1941 National Show and was Premier Sire of the Percheron Breed in 1947, 1948 and 1950. Lynnwood Don sired Lynnwood Dixiana II, the mother of Drake Farm's Chief.

Lynnwood Dixiana, a daughter of Don Again and winner of several championships at large Percheron shows including the National Show, was bred to her half-brother, Lynnwood Don, also a son of Don Again, to produce Lynnwood Dixiana II, the dam of Drake Farm's Chief. Lynnwood Dixiana is pictured here being held by Dixiana Taft, for whom the mare was named. Elmer Taft, manager of Lynnwood Farms, is standing next to his daughter.

There is no telling what Don Again may have accomplished as a breeding stallion had the Percheron industry been stronger during the 1940s and 50s. As it was, the horse lived during the worst period in Percheron business in America.

Charles J. Lynn, who owned Don Again throughout most of the animal's life, had established his herd of purebred Percherons at Lynnwood Farm in the early 1930s, when draft horse power was still commonplace.

Lynn's purchase of Don Again was out of the ordinary:

"It all really started with a Christmas package — the Percheron Fritzi, wrapped in bright red ribbon bows, presented proudly to Mr. Lynn by his family upon his return from a European visit. The owner of Lynnwood Farm, Carmel, Indiana, and one of the largest herds of Percherons in America, was so fond of Fritzi that he bought her sire, Don Again."[1]

From the start, Lynn started raising Percherons in a big way. His herd of breeding stock was one of the largest in America.

He was named Director of the Percheron Horse Association in 1937 and served until 1946 at which time he was named chairman of the Advisory Committee. Lynn was chosen Achievement Breeder in 1940 and in that same year his portrait

At one of many Lynnwood Sales held during the late 1930s and early 40s, five of the breed's most influential men stood for this photo. From left to right, Ellis McFarland, Worden Spitler, George Dix, Dean C.F. Curtiss, and Charles J. Lynn.

was hung in the Percheron Hall of Fame.

In addition, Lynn's portrait was hung in the famous portrait gallery at the Saddle and Sirloin Club at the Union Stock Yards in Chicago in 1954 in recognition of his achievements as a livestock breeder and as an agent of the Percheron Horse Association of America.

Lynn died in September 1958 from a heart attack when he was 84 years old. He was born and raised in Indianapolis, starting his business career as a $2 a week clerk and rising to the position of vice-president of Eli Lilly & Co., pharmaceutical manufacturers. He joined the Eli Lilly company in 1895.

In 1936, the same year he purchased Don Again, Lynn first suggested that a National Percheron Show be established:

"His far-sightedness in recommending such an annual showing is indicated by rises in transfers recorded in states sponsoring the Show: the National Show

A scene at the 1939 annual horse sale.

Lynnwood Farm's show string and stable decorations.

held at Pamona, Calif., in 1938 raised California from nineteenth to ninth place in the number of Percherons bought and sold in the United States; after the Show was held in Minnesota, this state moved up from sixth to fourth place."[2]

Lynn was determined to increase public interest in the Percheron at the time that interest was plummeting due to the decline of the work horse in general. Like his herd stallion, Don Again, Charles Lynn came on the Percheron scene too late. Both would have probably influenced the Percheron industry even more dramatically had they been around during the breed's heyday.

References

[1]Percheron News, October, 1944, p. 16.

[2]Ibid.

Photo Courtesy of Cook & Gormley

Charles Lynn (with the cane) and Lynnwood Horse Superintendent Elmer Taft stand with eight Lynnwood mares.

Appendix

Timeline of Percheron History in America

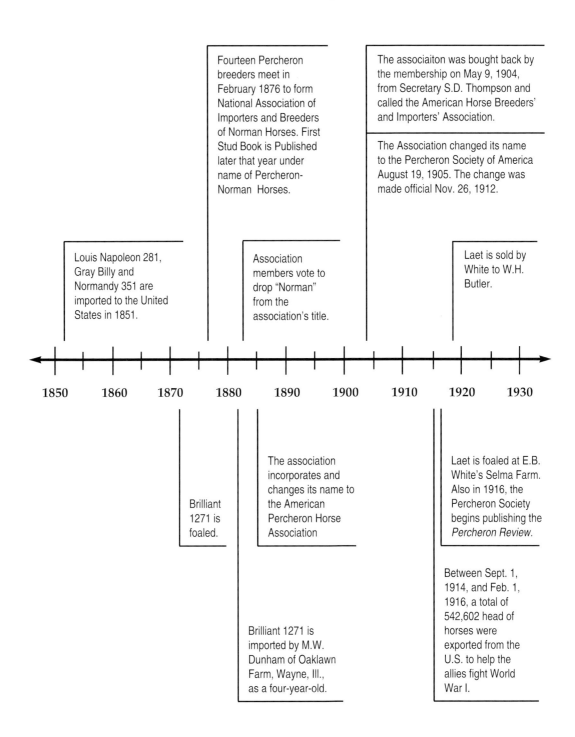

Fourteen Percheron breeders meet in February 1876 to form National Association of Importers and Breeders of Norman Horses. First Stud Book is Published later that year under name of Percheron-Norman Horses.

The associaiton was bought back by the membership on May 9, 1904, from Secretary S.D. Thompson and called the American Horse Breeders' and Importers' Association.

The Association changed its name to the Percheron Society of America August 19, 1905. The change was made official Nov. 26, 1912.

Louis Napoleon 281, Gray Billy and Normandy 351 are imported to the United States in 1851.

Association members vote to drop "Norman" from the association's title.

Laet is sold by White to W.H. Butler.

1850   1860   1870   1880   1890   1900   1910   1920   1930

Brilliant 1271 is foaled.

The association incorporates and changes its name to the American Percheron Horse Association

Laet is foaled at E.B. White's Selma Farm. Also in 1916, the Percheron Society begins publishing the *Percheron Review*.

Brilliant 1271 is imported by M.W. Dunham of Oaklawn Farm, Wayne, Ill., as a four-year-old.

Between Sept. 1, 1914, and Feb. 1, 1916, a total of 542,602 head of horses were exported from the U.S. to help the allies fight World War I.

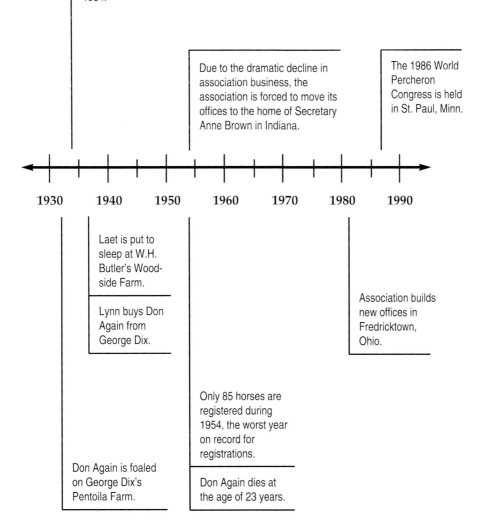

Chicago Union Stockyards fire of May 19, 1934, destroys Association offices.

Percheron Society of America reorganizes as a non-profit organization and changes its name to the Percheron Horse Association of America Dec. 14, 1934.

Due to the dramatic decline in association business, the association is forced to move its offices to the home of Secretary Anne Brown in Indiana.

The 1986 World Percheron Congress is held in St. Paul, Minn.

1930   1940   1950   1960   1970   1980   1990

Laet is put to sleep at W.H. Butler's Wood-side Farm.

Lynn buys Don Again from George Dix.

Association builds new offices in Fredricktown, Ohio.

Only 85 horses are registered during 1954, the worst year on record for registrations.

Don Again is foaled on George Dix's Pentoila Farm.

Don Again dies at the age of 23 years.

Officers of the Percheron Association

Secretary-Treasurers

George Stubblefield	1902-1910
Wayne Dinsmore	1910-1920
Ellis McFarland	1920-1948
Anne Brown	1948-1965
Dale Gossett	1965-1978
Lucille Gossett	1978-1982
Alex Christian	1982-

Secretary-Treasurers

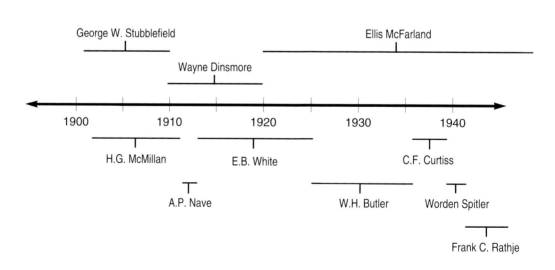

Presidents

Presidents

H.G. McMillan	1902-1912
A.P. Nave	1912-1913
E.B. White	1913-1926
W.H. Butler	1926-1936
C.F. Curtiss	1936-1939
Worden Spitler	1939-1942
Frank C. Rathje	1942-1952
Marshall Campbell	1952-1953
George Dix	1953-1955
John Taft	1955-1965
Ray Bast	1965-1984
J. William Read	1984-1990
Thomas Berry	1990-

Secretary-Treasurers

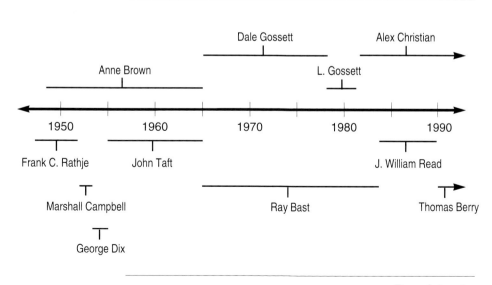

Presidents

Registrations

1911 —	7,608	1938 —	3,529	1965 —	185
1912 —	10,132	1939 —	3,534	1966 —	174
1913 —	9,754	1940 —	2,759	1967 —	181
1914 —	9,364	1941 —	2,472	1968 —	186
1915 —	8,492	1942 —	1,792	1969 —	175
1916 —	9,044	1943 —	1,389	1970 —	225
1917 —	10,508	1944 —	1,211	1971 —	223
1918 —	9,180	1945 —	845	1972 —	250
1919 —	9,151	1946 —	641	1973 —	254
1920 —	7,379	1947 —	449	1974 —	344
1921 —	5,364	1948 —	251	1975 —	318
1922 —	5,618	1949 —	253	1976 —	437
1923 —	5,433	1950 —	149	1977 —	501
1924 —	3,756	1951 —	125	1978 —	580
1925 —	3,815	1952 —	123	1979 —	750
1926 —	3,753	1953 —	108	1980 —	607
1927 —	4,022	1954 —	85	1981 —	826
1928 —	3,276	1955 —	99	1982 —	1,253
1929 —	2,853	1956 —	97	1983 —	1,261
1930 —	2,312	1957 —	112	1984 —	1,028
1931 —	2,114	1958 —	118	1985 —	1,132
1932 —	1,892	1959 —	131	1986 —	1,068
1933 —	2,651	1960 —	128	1987 —	1,206
1934 —	3,224	1961 —	126	1988 —	1,277
1935 —	4,836	1962 —	129	1989 —	1,088*
1936 —	5,028	1963 —	116	1990 —	1,346
1937 —	4,611	1964 —	142		

* In 1989 the Percheron Horse Association changed the end of its fiscal year from October 31 to August 31. Consequently, 1989 figures are for ten months only.

Premier Sires

1928 — Laet
1929 — Laet
1930 — Egotist
1931 — Don Degas
1932 — Laet
1933 — Laet
1934 — Laet
1935 — Baryton
1936 — Laet
1937 — Don Degas
1938 — Don Degas
1939 — Don Again
1940 — Don Again
1941 — Don Again
1942-1954 — No Shows
1946 — Topper
1947 — Lynnwood Don
1948 — Lynnwood Don
1949 — Koncarhope
1950 — Lynnwood Don
1951 — Don Again
1952 — Supreme Degas
1953 — Rowdy Degas
1954 — La Don
1955 — La Don

1956 — Double Carnot II
1957 — Lynnwood Don Again II
1958 — Topper
1959 — Lynnwood Don Again II
1960 — Lynnwood Don Again II
1961 — Lynnwood Don Again II
1962 — Lynnwood Don Again II
1963 — Ann's Silver
1964 — Drake Farm's Chief
1965 — Drake Farm's Chief
1966 — Drake Farm's Chief
1967 — Drake Farm's Chief
1968 — Drake Farm's Chief
1969 — Drake Farm's Chief
1970 — Drake Farm's Chief
1971 — Drake Farm's Chief
1972 — Drake Farm's Chief
1973 — Drake Farm's Chief
1973–1984 — No Award
1985 — Highview Dragano
1986 — Highview Dragano
1987 — Highview Dragano
1988 — Highview Dragano
1989 — Highview Dragano
1990 — Blackhome Duke

National Grand Champion Stallions

1936 — Milaet 215790
1937 — Corlaet 206052
1938 — Cozette's Diplomat Brown
1939 — Marceau 228765 (206103)
1940 — Marceau 228765 (206103)
1941 — Lynnwood Don 231169
1942 — Topper 237169
1946 — Lrevaet 232978
1947 — La Don 246244
1948 — La Don 246244
1949 — La Don 246244
1950 — La Don 246244
1951 — Director U.L.C.
1952 — Director U.L.C.
1953 — Geron Degas 247979
1954 — Double Carnot II 247183
1955 — La Kareno 248319
1956 — Easter 248517
1957 — Don Frelis 248494
1958 — Ann's Silver 248436
1959 — Ann's Silver 248436
1960 — Ann's Silver 248436
1961 — Ann's Silver 248436
1962 — Lincoln View La Rem 249352
1963 — Drake Farm's Chief 248516
1964 — Drake Farm's Chief 248516

1965 — Mr. Chief 249115
1966 — Jake 250054
1967 — Mr. Chief 249115
1968 — Easter Fury 250123
1969 — Lincoln View La Rem 249352
1970 — La Bells Big Chief
1971 — La Bells Big Chief
1972 — Ostraliens Count 250554
1973 — Ostraliens Count 250554
1974 — Maverick 251259
1975 — Maverick 251259
1976 — Maverick 251259
1977 — Maverick 251259
1978 — Renegade Koncarlaet 253305
1979 — Cash Koncarlaet
1980 — R.H.B. Chevaux
1981 — McGee
1982 — McGee
1983 — No Show
1984 — Glynlea's Pride
1985 — Blackhome Duke
1986 — Valley Vista Knightime
1987 — MG's Ukiah
1988 — Highwood Nick
1989 — Cousteau
1990 — Windsong's Gambler

Index

Allebach, Abraham 111
Arabian Breed 27-30

Barnhart, James....................................30, 111
Barnum & Bailey Circus...............................3
Bast, Helen...102
Bast, Jon 111, 113
Bast, Ray 102-105, 110, 112
Berry, Tom.................................111, 114-115
Bonheur, Isadore.....................................125
Bonheur, Rosa...................................129-134
Brilliant 1271 ....120-121, 125, 130-134
Brilliant 1899 120-121
Breed Type Studies..............................87-91
Brown, Dr. 35-37
Brock, Will 3
Brown, Anne......................97-98, 103-105
Burrows, G.T. 93
Buswell, John...139
Butler, W.H..............77, 89, 136-137, 139-145

Caine, A.B. 72
Calypso 25017...88
Campbell, B.H. 44
Carlson, G.L. 59
Carnona V...89-90
Carnot...148
Carthela 145
Chamberlin, Irvan 113
Chicago Union Stockyards Fire................82-85
Christian, Alex 109, 111, 114, 116-117
Christian, Elaine.................................109, 114
Circus 3
City Workhorses 7
Coddington, Ralph 111, 114
Coleman, C.R. 128
Congress, World Percheron 110-113, 115
Conner's Prairie Farm..................................90
Corsa, W.S.................................80, 88, 137
Corwin, Tom...80
Couceorous 138-140
Crusades...29
Curtiss, C.F. 73, 150
Cushman, A.P. 38
Cy Laet..145

Danforth, William 59
Darlington, Jesse......................................113
DeLancey, J.L. 58, 60, 63

Diligence 35
Dillon, Ellis...............................39, 42, 44
Dillon, Isaiah 42, 45
Dillon, Levi 38-39, 42
Dinsmore, Wayne....................4, 6,8,10, 71
Dix, George A...................102, 146-147, 150
Don Again 206636.........................146-152
Don Degas 186172 147-148
Draft Horse and Mule Assn. of America.........13
Dragon 139
Drake Farm's Chief.........................144, 149
Dunham, Daniel.......................................44
Dunham, Mark W. 42, 46, 120-134
Dunham, Solomon....................................123
Dunham, Wirth 74-76, 80, 128-129

Egan, Sylvester....................................61-62
Edwards, W.J. 42
Enchanter 212346...............................90-91

Finch Brothers 64-65
Fletcher, James 123, 128
Fockler, P.C. 120-121
Forwood, Marvyn....................................111
Fox, Charles (Chappie)..................................4
Fredricktown Office 108-109
French Embargo...5
French Revolution 29

Galbraith, Alex 18
Garen, Mary 93
Graham, F.B..59
Gray Billy..35-37
Godolphin and Gallipoly 29-30
Gossett, Dale 105
Gossett, Lucille 105, 108
Gregory Farm 80

Haroldson, Judy 111-112
Harris, Edward 34
Haxton, Dave...................112, 140-145
Hay, John..111
Hays, Charles du 30, 39
Hesitate Again 148
Hesitation...148
Hodgson, Eli...38
Holbert, Fred 18
Hoover, Andrew 92
Horse Association of America.............13, 74-76

Houston, D.F., U.S.
Military Horses 5,9,10

Jerome 145
Johnson, Leonard.....................................120
Jones, C.M. 63
Julie 234076 90-91

Kays, D.J..139
Keiser, C.O. 62
King Martel...27

Laet 133886 ....136-145, 148
Laet's Magic Queen.................................145
Lancinante 225458......................................90-91
Lee, Richard 111, 113
Le Perche..26
Le Pin...29
Louis Napoleon 281 ....35, 37-39
Lynn, Charles J. 146-152
Lynnwood Dixiana 149
Lyons, Robert W. 90

Mays, Dennis..113
McFarland, Ellis 13,16, 70, 77-80,
....85, 93-97, 150
McMillan, H.G. 45, 48-68, 88-89
Michigan State College.................................21
Milaet 145
Mischka, Robert 111-112
Moslem army...27

Nave, A.P. 58, 61, 63, 67
Nesus 231550 90-91
Normandy 351...35
Numbers of Horses ...13-15, 71, 85-86, 90, 100

Oaklawn Farm 46, 74, 80, 88, 120-134
Owen, James...42

Patterson, G.W. 59-67
Perriot, Edmond 124
Perry, James 42
Pine Tree Farms 90
Preference
for Percherons...16-20
Premier Laet 145
Prices 11

Prichard, W.E. 42, 58

Reed, J. William.................................109-111
Robbins, E.T..12
Robinson, Marilyn 111
Robison, J.C..63
Ruble, Simon...42

Samson 39
Sanders, James..42
Schumacher, Harold...................................111
Sears, Dr. Richard 113
Secretary of Agriculture 9
Sir Laet..145
Sir William..145
Spitler, Worden...150
Stubblefield, George....................................51
Stud Book, Vol. I 42

Taft, Dixiana..149
Taft, Elmer 149
Taylor, Phillip 113
Templeton, Peter...96
Thompson, Samuel D...............46, 52, 130-134
Tractors & Trucks 6,12-14, 71-81,
....85-87, 91, 101-102

Vickrey, Robert 111, 113-114

Walters, W.T..39
Wemple, A.J. 20
White, E.B. 72, 77, 136-140
Wolfington, Clark 80-81
World War I 4
World War II 21